MATERIAL VALUE

**More Sustainable, Less Wasteful
Manufacturing of Everything from
Cell Phones to Cleaning Products**

Julia L F Goldstein, PhD

Bebo Press

Material Value: More Sustainable, Less Wasteful Manufacturing of Everything from Cell Phones to Cleaning Products

Copyright © 2019 by Julia L F Goldstein, PhD

First edition, Bebo Press, Redmond, WA

This book was printed on demand, eliminating the negative environmental impact of printing large quantities of books that might go unsold and contribute to waste. When you finish reading it, please share this book with someone else who would enjoy it.

Cover design and interior typesetting: Alan Barnett
Interior graphics: Janine Milstrey
Editing: Ariel Hansen
Proofreading: Elaine Duncan
Indexing: Judi Gibbs

ISBN: 978-0-9995956-1-9 (Paperback)
ISBN: 978-0-9995956-2-6 (Hardcover)
ISBN: 978-0-9995956-3-3 (eBook)

Library of Congress Cataloging-in-Publication (CIP) data is available upon request.
LCCN: 2019901489

TABLE OF CONTENTS

PART I Setting the Stage

Chapter 8: Manufacturing and Processing Methods 155

PART IV Next Steps

Chapter 9: Regulations and Certifications 171

Chapter 10: Taking Action 195

INTRODUCTION

▨ Why this book, and why now

As the federal government in the US looks to dismantle many of the regulations around clean air, soil, and water that have been developed over the past few decades and businesses grapple with how to respond, we seem to be entering a new era. More and more, consumers want to know which chemicals and additives are in the products they buy and use, persuading various industries to become increasingly transparent about their products and their manufacturing methods. Manufacturing companies are taking a closer look at their operations. All types of businesses are considering more carefully where to buy the products they need, from coffee cups to furniture. Businesses of all sizes are reconsidering their materials usage, waste streams, and carbon footprints. However, some changes may be "feel-good" measures that do not make much of a difference.

This is the perfect time to publish a book looking at sustainability through a lens of materials extraction, processing, use, and disposal. My journey, however, started long before I began writing this book.

I first became fascinated by materials science—a field of engineering focused on materials selection, materials processing, and development of new materials—in college. I entered Harvey Mudd College in 1984 as a physics major. Second semester sophomore year I took a class called "Modern Physics" and realized that I didn't want to be a physics major. I wanted to study something more practical than quantum mechanics. I just wasn't driven to understand the world at that fundamental level.

Junior year, after switching my major to engineering, I took my first materials science course. Something about the idea of tailoring a material's physical properties by adding minute quantities of other materials or changing processing conditions fascinated me. And it didn't hurt that my professor,

1

Joe King, was young and enthusiastic. He was brand new to teaching but had worked in industry for several years after earning his PhD. He brought that real-world experience to a failure analysis course he taught my senior year.

Professor King had served as an expert witness in product liability cases. His expertise in examining fracture surfaces to determine when and how a product had failed was considered extremely valuable to companies being sued. Many years later, I learned *just* how valuable such expertise can be when I did some research for a law firm on a patent infringement case and was paid what seemed to me to be an exorbitant hourly rate.

Back when I was in college, I didn't think much about the ethical implications of materials selection and designing new materials. This now strikes me as peculiar given the mission of Harvey Mudd College, which hasn't changed over the decades. As stated on its website, "Harvey Mudd College seeks to educate engineers, scientists, and mathematicians well versed in all of these areas and in the humanities and the social sciences so that they may assume leadership in their fields with a clear understanding of the impact of their work on society."

I did, however, attend college in the 1980s, a decade not known for emphasizing environmentalism or social responsibility. That was for the hippies. My generation graduated with engineering degrees and pursued available job opportunities, many of which involved military contracts and required security clearances. The ethical and moral implications of their work just weren't at the forefront of most of my peers' minds as they pursued their careers.

I did think about product liability, given my exposure to failure analysis, and even took a course called "Ethical Issues in Engineering" when I was working on my MS in materials science at Stanford, but the sustainability piece hadn't occurred to me. Over the years, my perspective has shifted. I now believe that sustainable materials management is crucial. It needs to be addressed throughout the supply chain, from raw materials extraction through the entire life cycle of a manufactured product.

My voyage into materials toxicity began with my PhD research. One of Professor Bill Morris's students at University of California, Berkeley, had been researching the effect of additions of small quantities of other metals on the properties of tin-lead solders. That student was graduating, so Professor Morris asked me to step in to continue the research, which I agreed to do.

Then, a chance comment from another student at a weekly research group meeting changed the course of my research and my career. She mentioned that the US Congress was considering a ban on tin-lead solders in electronics, with the goal of eliminating lead, a toxic element. I decided almost on the spot that I needed to research lead-free solders. Would these alloys exhibit the same microscopic changes that tin-lead solders experienced when deformed at high temperature? I was curious.

The title of my PhD thesis, published in 1993, was "Microstructural Development and Mechanical Behavior of Eutectic Bismuth-Tin and Eutectic Indium-Tin in Response to High Temperature Deformation." In some ways, I was ahead of my time—it would take more than a decade before the Restriction of Hazardous Substances Directive, known as RoHS, was adopted in the European Union (EU). RoHS restricts the use of six hazardous materials in electronics, including lead. In other ways, my research was completely irrelevant, as is the case for many PhD research projects. Neither of the alloys I studied is a suitable replacement for tin-lead solder. Their melting points are too low.

Regardless of the significance of my research, my involvement in the early days of RoHS shaped my perspective. As an engineer, and later a journalist, in the field of semiconductor packaging, I became acutely aware of the struggles of the semiconductor industry to find a replacement that worked as well as tin-lead solder. I also became aware of the absurdity of the whole effort when put in a wider context. The amount of lead in solder joints is minuscule compared to the quantity of lead in lead-acid batteries, for example.

Throughout my career, I have been especially drawn to stories about new materials or better ways to use existing materials. In my freelance commercial writing business, I like to highlight ways in which my clients are reducing waste, saving energy, and creating manufacturing processes that are less toxic and more sustainable. I do this even when it is not part of the official agenda. When I'm interviewing engineers for a blog post covering some chemical compound or processing method, I ask questions about water use or how their company is managing toxic waste. Are they making sure toxins do not enter the local water supply, or are they working on finding ways to avoid using toxic compounds in the first place?

My clients' response to such questions influences my interest in pursuing further projects with them. Stories about companies that are apparently poisoning waterways without a second thought get my attention, and my instinct is to avoid those companies. But the story is not always as clear cut as it may seem. There are certainly examples where corporations appear to be acting with profit as the only goal despite harm to workers, the local communities, and the environment. In other cases, manufacturers may be negligent but not willfully so, and need guidance to better consider the consequences of their production methods or supply chain.

Materials and processing methods are usually chosen with performance as the key metric. Why has our society embraced plastics? Because they work. In most cases, they are lighter, easier to manufacture, and less expensive than the metal, wood, or stone they have replaced. Why do industrial manufacturers use toxic chemicals? Because they are effective. They efficiently clean surfaces or help create durable coatings. But the unintended consequences may be severe.

By learning how metals and plastics are made and what happens when various materials are recycled, readers will better understand the value of materials and the challenges that manufacturers face when trying to make their facilities and products less toxic and less wasteful. This is a huge subject, and I cannot possibly convey the whole story—entire books have been written about each of the topics in my chapters.

I've chosen instead to provide enough background that even readers who have forgotten everything they learned in high school chemistry can understand the concepts. Stories from my experience and that of the inspiring individuals I interviewed bring a personal touch to my narrative. I hope to awaken in my readers a new sense of the importance of materials selection, development, and processing.

As companies struggle to find replacements for materials, either to reduce real or suspected toxins or to reduce the amount of material wasted to manufacture a product, it can be hard to keep a proper perspective. Which efforts really matter, and which ones are a waste of time and effort? Which should be prioritized? I certainly don't have all the answers, but I hope that I can shed light on the problem and guide you, my readers, toward solutions that make a positive difference.

How this book is organized

This book is divided into four main parts, each broken into several chapters. Part I, "Setting the Stage," serves as an introduction to the parts that follow. The remaining chapters fill in the details: Part II covers materials, Part III focuses on manufacturing, and Part IV discusses the role of regulations and certifications and suggests strategies for readers wanting to incorporate a greater focus on sustainability in their lives.

Part I: Setting the stage, posing the problem

It is both extremely challenging and vitally important to get rid of environmental toxins. The first chapter puts the concepts of chemicals and chemistry into perspective. Not all toxins are created equal, and sometimes the consequences of removing a toxic material are counterintuitive or unexpected. Removing a toxin is not helpful if you only introduce a bigger problem in its place.

In the past decade, more and more companies have jumped on the "sustainability" bandwagon. Sometimes their efforts reflect an honest desire to reduce the environmental impact of their operations, but in other cases it still looks like greenwashing. Putting plans in place to deal with real and perceived dangers to employees, customers, and local communities is no longer optional, and corporate executives understand the need to say that sustainability matters.

The scope of sustainability covers a wide range of concerns, and corporate sustainability programs don't all look alike. Transparency is tricky, especially when combined with the concern about keeping proprietary information away from competitors. Chapter 2 discusses the importance of transparency and gives examples where things have gone horribly wrong, but also where companies have taken a better route by openly admitting failures and explaining the steps they have taken to improve their products and processes.

The Four Systems Conditions provides an excellent framework for considering the importance of not making existing environmental problems worse. The fewer natural resources manufacturing requires, the less chance there is for excess waste, toxic or not, to pollute the Earth. That's the premise behind Chapter 3, which also addresses lean manufacturing practices.

Part II: The materials we use

Every physical object or substance on the planet is formed from some combination of elements in the periodic table. Natural materials like rocks and minerals, created deep in the Earth millions of years ago, predate human history. People have been using materials in creative ways since prehistoric times, but civilization has come a long way since our ancient ancestors used wood and stone to create tools.

All the items we use in our daily lives are made from materials. Some are created from natural materials, changed very little from how they appear in nature. But most of the objects that humans interact with are made from engineered materials. These materials have been transformed through manufacturing processes, in many cases designed to serve specific purposes. Plastics are an obvious example of a highly processed material that looks and feels nothing like its original source. But glass and metal, while created from naturally occurring minerals, undergo extensive manufacturing processes before they become raw materials for creating useful objects.

Part II of this book focuses on two primary classes of engineered materials: plastics and metals, with a chapter devoted to each. Many of the chemicals that cause health problems are those that are added, intentionally or unintentionally, to metals and plastics during processing. Certain metals, lead in particular but many others as well, are toxic on their own. Whether present as unwanted contaminants or additives designed to improve performance, there is a reason to be concerned about toxic substances.

Plastics and metals are the primary building blocks for many everyday objects. For example, a smartphone contains dozens of different metals, in quantities ranging from substantial to minuscule, and several plastics. Automobiles are made of many metal and plastic parts. Manufacturing of all sorts of products necessarily involves equipment made from these two classes of materials.

There are certainly other types of materials that are important in our society. The construction industry, for example, couldn't have developed as it has without concrete and glass. Ceramics are used in applications ranging from cookware to packaging for computer chips. Computer chips rely on the semiconductor silicon for their computing power. And although our society is well into the information age and supposedly weaning ourselves off physical documents, we remain attached to paper and continue to use a great deal of it. This book does touch on these materials briefly, but they are not my primary focus.

Part III: Rethinking manufacturing and recycling

The environmental impact of the products we use lies not only in their ingredients but in how the products are manufactured and how they are handled at the end of their useful life. No discussion of efficient manufacturing would be complete without addressing recycling. Part III opens with two chapters on recycling, looking at both why and how.

Chapter 6 dives into the details of the recycling process, with extensive discussion on the challenges involved in recycling various materials. Plastics, for example, are especially troublesome to recycle efficiently.

The topic of electronic waste (e-waste) is deeply entwined in both reducing waste and handling hazardous materials and deserves a separate chapter. While e-waste is a huge global problem, there are excellent solutions on the horizon, which is encouraging. Chapter 7 highlights the problems with existing e-waste infrastructure and points to ways in which it can be improved.

Chapter 8 focuses on industrial manufacturing and examines ways to reduce waste. Many conventional manufacturing processes are subtractive—the process starts with a block or sheet of material that is etched or machined away to leave the desired shape or pattern. These processes necessarily produce waste in the form of excess material removed that does not form part of the finished product. Much of this waste, however, can often be recycled in-house and reused, creating the most efficient form of recycling.

Additive manufacturing has the potential to be much more environmentally friendly. Materials are deposited layer by layer, making the process naturally less wasteful than subtractive manufacturing. Various additive processes are likely to play an increasingly important role in manufacturing from here on out. Still, 3-D printing—a subset of additive manufacturing—is not without its drawbacks and could lead to increases in materials usage if excitement over its possibilities creates a huge demand for 3-D printers in every household. Building and operating printers requires an expense of materials and energy. Unless the printers are used to create products that would otherwise be made with more wasteful methods, they may be inadvertently increasing waste.

Part IV: Next steps to motivate change

Many companies have taken steps to make manufacturing less wasteful, but there is still plenty of room for improvement and opportunity to effect greater change. Change can come about through internal or external motivation. In the case of businesses and industries, external motivation arrives in the form of laws and regulations designed to restrict undesirable practices or certifications designed to encourage desirable practices. While a segment of the business community will be internally motivated to "do the right thing" as part of company culture, external motivators are needed to effect widespread change. Chapter 9 puts into perspective various industry and government efforts to regulate and certify businesses. Are certifications and reporting standards achieving their desired goals, or are they creating unnecessary paperwork and falling short?

The final chapter aims to help readers translate the information from the previous chapters into action. In our roles as citizens, employers, employees, and consumers, we have the power to encourage positive change. Entrepreneurs can consider how they want to incorporate choices in materials, manufacturing, and suppliers into their company's culture as they grow. Those working at a company can use what they learn to propose new practices at their workplace or decide it is time for a career change. Consumers can influence supply and demand through what they choose to buy or avoid and can educate themselves to better understand how their purchases can make a difference. Everyone has a role to play in moving toward a vision of more sustainable, less wasteful manufacturing.

PART I

Setting the Stage

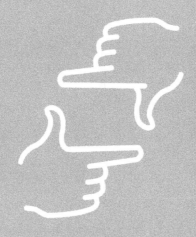

CHAPTER 1

Chemicals—The Helpful and the Harmful

"We have a long way to go in terms of building our awareness around chemicals and creating a harmonized approach to the chemicals of concern."
—*Jeff Frost, Mindful MATERIALS and Brightworks Sustainability*

Helpful and harmful chemicals

Everything on Earth is made from chemicals. Some chemical compounds, like water, sustain life. The human body is made of chemicals. The problem arises when we ingest or absorb the wrong types of chemicals, or in the wrong quantities. Some elements in the periodic table are metals that the body needs. Others, such as lead and arsenic, can kill.

Some compounds are obviously toxic, but too much of *anything* can be dangerous. Drinking too much water can cause hyponatremia, a potentially deadly condition that occurs when water dilutes the electrolytes in the blood, causing sodium levels to drop to a dangerously low level. This is why endurance athletes consume sports drinks and not just plain water.

But the real problem with chemicals comes when people are exposed to specific elements or chemical compounds, either through accidental contamination or purpose-driven use. Certain chemicals, often labeled "substances of concern," are toxic to humans and other living creatures even in extremely minute quantities.

Some naturally occurring compounds are toxic, but for the most part, dangerous chemicals are those that have been developed in laboratories and were never intended to exist in nature. The companies making industrial chemicals don't often sufficiently weigh the toxicity of the compounds they are producing.

Many consumer-goods companies make products from synthetic or chemically derived ingredients. But they don't see themselves as chemical companies. For example, Procter & Gamble doesn't talk about the chemicals in their shampoo formulations because that's not a message their customers want to hear. Still, the company couldn't make commercial shampoo without either naturally-derived or synthetic chemicals.

The drive toward removing chemicals from products has led to more products being labeled as "natural" and "simple." They tend to have fewer ingredients than the products they are replacing, but that doesn't necessarily make them safer or healthier. So-called "natural" products are often safer than conventional ones made with industrial chemicals, but that is not always the case.

The air we breathe

In his book *The Unnatural World*, author David Biello emphasizes that humans have been changing the natural world for tens of thousands of years, beginning with the establishment of agriculture. He recognizes, however, that these changes have been accelerating since the second half of the twentieth century. "Our need for fire has left a consistent black smudge that covers the globe," writes Biello. That smudge is the result of soot, particles of carbon created from combustion. Anyone who has ever stood around a campfire has seen soot and probably gotten it on their fingers or clothing.

In the summer and fall of 2017, the western US suffered from unprecedented fires. They destroyed acres of forest and thousands of homes and made the air dangerous to breathe for days on end. It was the first time I ever saw smog in Seattle. I was not the only one to say that the air in Seattle and Portland looked like Los Angeles in the 1970s. Unfortunately, summer smoke in the Pacific Northwest may be the new norm, as 2018 looked as bad as the previous year. In California, it looked even worse.

When I was growing up in Southern California, the Los Angeles basin was nearly always smog ridden. A brown haze hung over the horizon, especially in the inland regions far from the breezes of the Pacific Ocean. We experienced something called Santa Ana winds, where instead of coming from the west, the prevailing wind pattern changed, bringing in hot air from the deserts east of Los Angeles. These brought both intense heat and increased smog.

I attended college in Claremont, which is as far east as you can travel while remaining in Los Angeles County. The smog there at the time was so bad that many days we could not even see the San Gabriel Mountains, a mere 11 miles north of campus. When the occasional rains came and cleaned up the smog momentarily, the mountains reappeared as though by magic. It amazed me how close they were. Today's Claremont College students and Inland Valley residents enjoy far cleaner air most of the time.

Overall improvements in air quality in California in the past few decades have occurred thanks to reduced sulfur dioxide (SO_2) emissions. In the US, such emissions were halved between 1970 and 2000. It is not a coincidence that a process called flue gas desulfurization became commonplace in the US in the 1970s. This process removed sulfur from the gases emitted from coal-fired power plants. More stringent regulations on emissions from vehicle exhaust also contributed to healthier air quality.

In China and India, however, SO_2 emissions continued to rise rapidly well into the twenty-first century as these countries brought electricity and cars to more and more of their citizens. Anyone who has been to large cities in China recently can attest to the poor air quality, at levels that make even 1970s and 1980s Los Angeles air seem clean. The flue gas desulfurization process was finally added to Chinese power plants in 2007, but this hasn't yet been sufficient to clean up the air.

The decrease in sulfur emissions led coal proponents to talk about "clean coal." Coal, however, is certainly not a clean source of energy. Nor is it efficient—the amount of energy that can be generated by burning a ton of coal is less than half that from a ton of natural gas. Coal is finally becoming a poor choice from an economic standpoint, which is good news for public health. The sooner our society can transition to cleaner burning energy sources, the better.

Shifting away from coal toward other sources of fuel is merely one example of a drive toward reducing the amount of toxins in the air, water, and soil. Many more environmental toxins pose a risk to people all over the world. It sounds like the obvious answer for better public health is to remove them. That goal, however, is not easy to achieve.

Toxic materials: remove or replace?

Getting rid of environmental toxins is hard, harder than you might think. There are multiple reasons for this: the extensive presence of certain toxins, difficulty removing toxins, uncertainty regarding toxicity of certain materials, the challenge of finding safer replacements, and resistance from industries that benefit financially from materials that happen to be toxic.

The extensive presence of toxins

Certain toxic materials have infiltrated cities around the world. Removing the toxins requires a huge expense of time and money. Who is going to pay for it? The polluters themselves will likely do so only if regulations compel them to act. Government funding for cleanup and replacement of infrastructure can be hard to come by. Private companies aren't going to be motivated to tackle the problem if there isn't any money to be made in doing so.

Nongovernmental organizations (NGOs) dedicated to improving public health and the environment have an interest in creating solutions. Sufficiently large NGOs may be able to make a dent, but even well-funded organizations face funding limits and a lack of qualified staff. Partnering with universities provides a source of funding, but university research is notoriously slow.

The prevalence of lead in water systems is a prime example of a toxic material that has become ubiquitous. The pipes themselves have not been made from lead in a very long time. Modern plumbing uses plastic or copper piping. Even plumbing solder for copper pipes has been lead-free in the US since 1986 as result of the Safe Drinking Water Act Amendments. Despite these changes, many miles of legacy water pipes contain lead. Replacing this infrastructure is an overwhelming and expensive task, but one that is necessary for public health. The story of Flint, Michigan, (see Chapter 5) is an example of what can go wrong if old pipes aren't replaced.

Removing toxins

The life cycle of toxic materials follows many possible paths. In some cases, companies have dumped toxin-laden waste into their communities for decades, either accidentally or on purpose, ignoring the associated risk. In these cases, toxins often leach into soil and groundwater to such an extent that they are hard to find, let alone isolate and remove. Areas with large enough concentrations are easier to clean up, but trace quantities often remain in sufficient concentration to be harmful.

Some products are only obviously toxic or hazardous during manufacturing. Once the product is in the customer's hands, it is perfectly safe. Dangerous solvents have evaporated or been cleaned off. Reactive chemicals have completed the reaction process, leaving nontoxic substances in their place. If the only issue with a specific chemical is worker exposure, it is easier to put in safeguards for workers than to change the product. Such safeguards include properly venting work areas or having employees wear protective gear. Another "solution," which doesn't actually solve the problem but merely moves it, is to manufacture products in countries where worker protection regulations are nonexistent or poorly enforced. Unfortunately, this approach has been all too common.

Some products that contain toxic compounds are stable and safe during use, only to reveal their toxic nature when the product is discarded into a landfill or burned. QLED televisions made with cadmium selenide quantum dots contain very small quantities of cadmium, but the toxic element is embedded deep inside the product, so users aren't at risk for exposure. The risk of cadmium exposure during e-waste processing of televisions is also small compared to the other hazards present at many e-waste facilities (see Chapter 7).

Burning trash for energy can be considered a better alternative than extracting and burning coal and oil from the standpoint of greenhouse gas emissions, but it comes with risks. Fumes emitted from burning can be dangerous, so it's important to capture and filter the smoke to minimize the risk of exposure to toxins.

Where are the replacements?

Toxic materials aren't chosen for their toxicity (except in the case of pesticides and the like), but for their beneficial properties or lower cost. Manufacturers are resistant to replacing something that works well, especially in the absence of a strong case that end users are exposed to any toxins. Fortunately, there are many examples of nontoxic products that are as effective, or sometimes more effective, than the conventional products they are replacing. Environmentally friendly products have improved significantly, and consumers have more reasons than ever before to give them a chance. Later chapters discuss specific examples.

Minimizing exposure during manufacturing is helpful. Avoiding the use of toxic chemicals in the first place is better. Sometimes, however, drop-in replacements aren't available. If no commercial material exists to replace a toxic one, a company can either continue using the offending material or stop production while waiting for someone to develop a replacement. In most cases, companies decide that the second option doesn't make sense financially. If they lack the expertise in-house to develop new materials and don't have the clout to convince their suppliers to do so, companies are stuck with a functional but problematic material. They need to implement the best safety practices available until a better solution becomes available.

Cause and effect

Cause and effect can be hard to prove, and correlation does not necessarily imply causation. Studies that suggest a lack of evidence of toxicity are not necessarily impartial. Companies have a vested interest in demonstrating that their products are safe and often fund studies that are designed to show that no danger to consumers exists. In situations where a substance is undeniably toxic, and studies consistently show this, industries lobby to suppress or refute results.

Companies producing tetraethyl lead as a gasoline additive knew that the chemical was toxic before it became a commercial product. They decided to go ahead with commercializing it. The companies assumed that they could control exposure to lead in their manufacturing plants through proper safety procedures. They further assumed that the amount of lead in the final product was so small as to not be a public health hazard.

Both assumptions proved false. In 1924, several workers at a tetraethyl lead production facility died as a result of exposure. The company involved managed to avoid publicity, and production continued. Later, the public health hazard became clear. Even in the face of data linking elevated levels of lead in the blood of US citizens to exposure to leaded gasoline, tetraethyl lead production continued. Finally, the US Clean Air Act of 1970 forced the gradual phasing out of lead in gasoline.

Uncertainties and the lack of knowledge

Companies developing safer alternatives to existing products sometimes exaggerate the dangers inherent in the conventional materials. The warnings feed on consumers' fears and raise red flags where they aren't warranted. In some cases, the new materials come with dangers of their own.

The chemical industry produces tens of thousands of different compounds, and it is nearly impossible to track them all. Product manufacturers, whether in construction, transportation, or electronics, have developed their own lists of chemicals that are not allowed. These so-called red lists specify chemicals that are forbidden because of their established level of toxicity.

Companies that buy chemicals will ideally consider all the toxins that are known and develop a definitive list that will guide their purchasing decisions. But suppliers are constantly developing new formulations.

Attempts to create industry-wide red lists have often failed. As an example, Green Wizard created a database of more than 100,000 green building products, aimed at an audience of architects and developers. The funding that Green Wizard would have needed to leverage industry experience and create a meaningful list wasn't forthcoming, however, and the company went out of business in 2015.

The primary players in chemical regulation have developed vastly different versions of red lists. Some of the most obviously toxic materials appear on all lists, but beyond those, there is very little overlap. If organizations that have been studying chemical safety for years can't agree on a list of hazardous chemicals, how can a manufacturer trying to evaluate its supply chain know what choices to make? They need to make the best decisions they feel will address employee and customer safety while meeting product performance and cost goals. There will necessarily be trade-offs.

Resistance from industry

The technical hurdles of inventing new materials and removing toxins are substantial, but the policy hurdles look even harder to overcome. Many years of research and development have gone into creating existing products and manufacturing processes. Industries tend to become entrenched and fight aggressively against policies that will force them to redesign their product lines. Even if safer materials exist, the path is not straightforward.

Changing materials is relatively easy if the new material is a drop-in replacement, meaning that the production process remains unchanged or only needs minor adjustments. An as example, companies can substitute a safer chemical in a metal electroplating bath by adjusting plating time but keeping everything else the same. Other changes, such as implementing a different type of plating method to properly coat parts with new materials, requires a huge capital expense to buy new equipment and months or years to develop and refine new processing methods.

Some changes, like replacing fossil fuels, threaten the existence of entire industries. If our society stops generating energy from coal, the companies whose only product is coal will go out of business unless they can pivot rapidly to another source of income.

Despite the above challenges, pressure exists to create healthier, less toxic products in safer manufacturing environments. Businesses that have traditionally been tagged as the evildoers who create products that endanger public health—the chemical and energy industries come to mind—are shifting gears.

The list of companies that are making great strides in removing toxic chemicals and reducing emission of hazardous substances is growing longer every year. The following chapters include stories from many such companies and also of industry-wide collaborations that benefit not only the companies involved but their customers and the communities in which they operate.

Calling out hazards and risks

Manufacturers of industrially produced materials are required to create a Safety Data Sheet (SDS) for each product. These documents, which used to be called Materials Safety Data Sheets, spell out the hazards and precautions associated with specific chemicals. The SDS lists the chemical compounds present in the material and explains hazards associated with using it, such as risk of fire, or adverse health effects from inhaling vapors or dust generated from mechanical grinding. The document must specify safe handling procedures for any foreseen use of the product.

Manufacturers can't hide anything in an SDS. If a material produces toxic fumes during use, the SDS calls that out. If a product contains formaldehyde, the SDS must say so. An experience at a conference reminded me of the importance of checking the details.

I met Laura Clise, the former Director of Sustainability at Weyerhaeuser, at a GoGreen conference in Seattle where she gave a presentation. Laura brought an unusual prop up on stage—a wooden duck she called Penny Parallam. Weyerhaeuser makes a product called Parallam, which it calls a "natural engineered wood product." Penny is made entirely from this material.

Wood veneers, those thin strips of high-grade wood covering cheaper plywood (or sometimes particle board) in furniture, must look good. That means that a significant portion of the tree is unusable for creating veneers. Weyerhaeuser takes the lower-value strips and presses them into panels, creating Parallam.

Making use of the entire tree once it is cut down sounds like a good use of resources and a positive step toward Weyerhaeuser's goal of responsible forestry. The phrase "engineered wood," however, brings up visions of formaldehyde-laced particle board.

Since Weyerhaeuser was calling Parallam "natural," I figured it must be free from formaldehyde, but when I visited the Weyerhaeuser website I learned that is not the case. The SDS for Parallam says that it contains 7–8 percent phenol-formaldehyde solids by weight. The data sheet also includes warnings about the carcinogenic nature of wood dust and recommends using a respirator when cutting or sanding the product in an environment without proper ventilation. In all fairness, untreated wood poses the same dangers, which most people sawing in their garages probably ignore.

The SDS provides useful information for customers, even though consumers buying products for use at home are unlikely to read the data sheets. As I learned from interviewing materials expert Jeff Frost, however, the limits inherent in the SDS can be frustrating for those trying to design with non-toxic products.

INTERVIEW Jeff Frost, Mindful MATERIALS and Brightworks Sustainability

Despite the existence of SDSs, it can be difficult to find out what is really in products sold to consumers and whether something advertised as non-toxic or "safe" lives up to that promise. That is the premise behind Mindful MATERIALS, an industry-led initiative to develop a database of materials used in building construction.

Jeff Frost wears two green hats: one as project manager and healthy materials specialist at Brightworks Sustainability and another as co-chair of the Mindful MATERIALS administrative working group. Jeff has experienced up close how difficult it is to get information from materials manufacturers.

As Jeff explained to me, builders wanting to create more healthy homes and workplaces would like to eliminate toxic chemical compounds from their buildings but don't necessarily have the guidance they need to do so. Construction materials don't come with ingredient lists. But as more materials manufacturers enter details about their products into the Mindful MATERIALS database, builders will gain access to better data.

Jeff has been involved with promoting less-toxic materials since the early 2000s. His journey started with addressing chemical sensitivity in the context of architecture and building construction. At that time, eco-friendly construction was focused on making buildings energy-efficient and reducing the carbon footprint, with no thought about toxic chemicals. Leadership in Energy and Environmental Design certification for green buildings—better known by its acronym, LEED—was just getting started.

Improvements in energy efficiency in buildings have ironically come at the expense of creating a less healthy indoor environment. By shutting off the flow of cold or hot air between a building and the outdoors, toxins have little opportunity to escape. Anyone who has had to cope with the smell of new paint or new carpet and worried about what fumes are coming from those products can relate to the need to think about indoor air quality.

Back in 2002, Jeff struggled to find information about what was in the products being installed in residential or commercial buildings. There was no available database of chemical compounds. The information in SDSs was minimally helpful, listing hazards but not the details Jeff wished he could get his hands on. Manufacturers were not required to supply ingredient lists and were not going to do so voluntarily. They wanted to keep their proprietary formulas away from their competitors. That motivation overshadowed any desire for transparency to customers.

Jeff landed in Portland, Oregon, in 2004 and discovered retail stores selling nontoxic materials for home construction and remodeling. He was immediately inspired and soon joined forces with Mick Dalrymple, who was based in Phoenix, Arizona. In 2005, Jeff and Mick co-founded aka Green, a green building store near Phoenix. The store stayed in operation until 2010, when the economic downturn proved to be too much to keep business going. Jeff describes the experience as a "five-year crash course in chemicals of concern." It forced him to work with manufacturers and create his own list of recommended products.

After closing aka Green, Jeff joined architecture and planning company SmithGroupJJR and focused on LEED documentation. He worked with Russell Perry, a leader in the green building industry since the 1990s, to put together Health Product Declarations and lists of "chemicals of concern."

Jeff now devotes most of his professional life to materials safety: creating healthy and sustainable materials programs, evaluating materials for clients, and educating contractors and designers.

Although much more information is available now than when Jeff started his journey into eco-friendly materials, he finds that it can still be difficult to know if promised solutions to an existing hazard really meet the goals they claim.

When Jeff reviews products, he evaluates what certifications they have earned in the marketplace. He finds that approach more effective than screening against a list of specific chemicals.

When Jeff goes through an evaluation for a Brightworks client, he considers health impact, carbon footprint, water use, waste generation, and materials management. Different clients may define sustainability through slightly varying lenses, and by considering all these factors, Brightworks give clients a more holistic picture of the choices they are making.

Regardless of certifications earned, manufacturers must understand their entire supply chain. Mindful MATERIALS has a role to play in helping those in the building construction industry make better choices when buying materials. Jeff hopes that this type of effort will expand into other industries.

As of late 2017, Mindful MATERIALS was starting to introduce the "chemicals of concern" criteria into the furniture industry. It remains to be seen how much of an effect Mindful MATERIALS will have on manufacturing, but it is a step in the right direction.

Looking at progress

Removing toxins requires a major investment of time and money. In the long run, however, such investment will pay off. Public health risks will decrease. In many cases, the businesses involved will be able to continue their operations. Ideally, they can keep the best aspects of their businesses and replace what needs fixing to create products that are safer and healthier.

Fortunately, progress has been made in my lifetime. For example:

- Gasoline no longer contains lead.
- Levels of sulfur dioxide in the atmosphere are lower, due to improved controls on vehicle emissions and reduced usage of coal for heating, greatly improving air quality in the US.
- Water treatment in cities has improved.

- Raw materials are produced more efficiently, using less energy per unit of material produced.
- Recycling of paper, metal, and plastic has become commonplace in many cities.

These steps are encouraging, but efforts need to go further. Part of the problem is that unless the threat is dire, many businesses and governments are not going to invest the time and money required to do something about it. They sometimes take tiny steps and pat themselves on the back. A business that uses recycled paper in its North American offices but still emits plumes of toxic smoke from its factories or subjects its workers in far-flung countries to inhumane, unsafe conditions is hardly doing the right thing. Businesses need to look at the big picture and delve into how the materials and the manufacturing processes that they, or their suppliers, use affect people and the planet.

2006 versus 2016

I am far from the first author to talk about sustainable or nontoxic materials. *Green to Gold* by Daniel Esty and Andrew Winston, published in 2006, has served as a blueprint for companies wanting to evaluate their environmental record and fix any shortcomings, with an eye on long-term revenue growth. Changes in sustainability efforts and reporting may or may not have directly resulted from Esty and Winston's book, but I imagine that the authors appreciate the progress.

In 2006:

- Compliance with the Restriction of Hazardous Substances (RoHS) regulation went into effect. RoHS required companies selling consumer electronics in the European Union (EU) to remove specific key toxins from their products.
- The Global Reporting Initiative (GRI) launched the G3 reporting framework guidelines governing sustainability reporting for businesses.
- 1,000 international companies were registered with GRI.
- Starbucks published its sixth annual Corporate Social Responsibility (CSR) report, but it was in the minority. CSR reporting was still in its infancy.
- The Governance and Accountability Institute, a sustainability consulting firm, was founded.
- B Lab, the nonprofit that certifies Benefit Corporations (B Corps), was founded. Companies first became registered as B Corps in 2010.

In 2016:

- According to a study by the Governance and Accountability Institute, more than 80 percent of US Fortune 500 companies published Sustainability Reports, compared to less than 20 percent in 2011, the first year the institute compiled data.

- GRI launched the GRI Standards in October. These replace the G4 guidelines, an update from the G3 guidelines. Companies reporting after June 2018 must use the new standards. Chapter 9 delves more deeply into GRI standards implementation and how the act of reporting can drive concrete, positive changes.

The concept of CSR has clearly taken hold even in companies that have not historically been associated with prioritizing the common good. Companies increasingly want to be seen as being good corporate citizens that look out for their employees, customers, and the communities in which they operate.

As we will see in Chapter 2, however, this doesn't always translate into taking responsibility when things go wrong. Many companies emphasize the areas of CSR where they excel. They go silent, or keep discussion to a minimum, in areas where they are falling short.

Even though the world has changed in the decade-plus since *Green to Gold* was published, the environmental issues that Esty and Winston identified remain relevant and are more urgent than ever. The authors emphasized important topics such as climate change, energy and water use, toxic chemicals, pollution, and waste management. In the coming chapters, I address all these issues.

CHAPTER 2

The Message You Send

"Sustainability is a mutual problem. We all own it."
—*Mallen Baker, CSR Consultant*

"The complexity of sustainability issues is real, but that doesn't mean you have to tell a complex story."
—*Joost de Kluijver, Closing the Loop*

The sheen of transparency

I do not believe that capitalism is inherently good or inherently evil. Business fulfills an important role in society. Companies large and small produce goods and services that people either need to survive or want to own to improve their quality of life. At the same time, many industries exploit the natural resources of the planet with seemingly little concern for the negative consequences of their practices. The path forward can take a positive direction, but that requires transparency. Greenwashing, in which companies tout advances in sustainability while continuing damaging practices—producing vast streams of toxic waste or burning excessive quantities of fossil fuels, for example—is a real concern.

This chapter looks at the stories that companies tell and shares some specific examples in industries including agriculture, consumer products, and transportation. These stories emphasize the importance of not only doing the right thing but communicating actions in a way that is honest and resonates with those affected.

Transparency is an important concept as people try to distinguish what is really going on behind the scenes. In a world that seems in so many ways like George Orwell's *1984*, how do we know the truth? Transparency is a valid goal. People appreciate stories where companies talk honestly about what went wrong and how they are fixing it. We hope that the next generation of products will have nothing to hide.

But what *is* hiding behind the sheen of transparency? The magician says, "There's nothing up my sleeve" and reveals a bare arm, hoping that the audience will focus its attention on the sleeve and not notice as she sneaks something into her pocket with expert sleight-of-hand. A company says, "Look, here are the windows, we cleaned them, you can see everything that's inside. Tour our facilities, look at our shiny new certifications." Yes, everything you can see looks good. But what if all the clear windows are meant to distract the viewer from the one window in the corner where the shades are drawn? What nefarious problems or toxins are hiding behind that window?

Companies, like performing magicians, need not share everything. That destroys competitive advantage. Companies can't let their customers in to see all that happens behind the scenes. They justifiably need to keep proprietary trade secrets away from the prying eyes of their competitors. If they divulge everything that's in a proprietary formula, including how to process all the ingredients, a competitor could make the same product at a lower price.

The trick involves achieving the right balance. How can a company honestly share its story, and convince customers its products are pure, safe, and wholesome, without giving away too much? For companies that have no skeletons in their closet, this shouldn't be too difficult. They can share a story explaining how they evaluated the products on the market, considered how to make theirs more effective, and always chose a path that avoided toxic ingredients or wasteful manufacturing processes.

Some companies have championed such efforts from the beginning. These companies are always under pressure to keep to their principles, though. They can't let the lure of extra profit tempt them to consider a material or process that doesn't mesh with the values their brand promotes.

Tactics for messaging depend on whether a company is operating in a business-to-business or business-to-consumer model. Companies selling materials or products to other businesses need to provide a level of detail that will give engineers or chemists the information they need to make an informed buying decision. Selling directly to consumers requires a less detailed message.

Reaching your audience

Consumers need information presented in a way that they can understand. Most people aren't stupid, but they may be ignorant. An ingredient list means little if the audience doesn't know the difference between one ingredient and another. Just because an ingredient has a long name, that doesn't mean it is toxic. Nor does labeling something "natural" mean it must be safe. Oleander is natural, but I wouldn't want to see it in anything I'm eating or applying to my skin. Many consumers, however, do not understand the limitations of the "natural" label.

Companies should clearly explain which things they have done to make a "greener" product, why they have taken the steps they have, and which steps aren't possible right now. That way, the customer will be in a better position to make an informed decision. Positioning one product as "sustainable" or "safe" and competing products as "unsustainable" or "unsafe" is oversimplifying the situation.

Customers wanting to know more details need to understand the challenges that manufacturers face. What limits their efforts? Manufacturers face constraints on materials, technology, or costs. Materials may not be commercially available. Technology may not be able to produce certain products reliably or in high enough volume. The costs in making a change may be too high for the market to bear.

Regardless of audience, messaging should be clear rather than confusing or contradictory. Joost de Kluijver, the CEO of Closing the Loop, emphasizes easily understandable messaging in his work addressing the life cycle of the cell phone. My interview with Joost appears in Chapter 7.

Creating inspiring taglines

Companies wanting to position themselves as being environmentally friendly and concerned with the way they are treating their workers, customers, and communities often adopt far-reaching taglines or slogans. These are designed to make customers feel good about choosing to buy products or services from the company. Customers believe they are buying from an ethical company and are therefore making an ethical decision. But do company taglines really ring true?

Here is my take on a few taglines, all of which contain a promise.

Umicore: "Materials for a better life"
Who doesn't want a better life? Umicore provides a range of goods and services centered around materials technology and recycling. They produce catalysts for emissions control on vehicles, helping them run more cleanly and meet emissions standards. Umicore recycles precious metals and other specialty metals, addressing the issue of resource scarcity and the damage done by mining. These efforts make a positive difference, but Umicore's methods aren't necessarily the best available (more on this in Chapter 7).

HP: "Technology that makes life better for everyone, everywhere"
This sounds a bit presumptuous, but HP does explain that this is a vision they strive toward. Even if more technology doesn't necessarily make life better—I find my HP printer useful, but it isn't much of a factor in my overall quality of life—the company has engaged in some forward-thinking practices around product design and reuse, which I discuss in later chapters.

DuPont: "The miracles of science"
This tagline replaced the oft-quoted and sometimes satirized "Better living through chemistry" tagline that the company used from 1935 to 1982. It reads as fuzzier and less prone to becoming satire. Now that Dow and DuPont have merged, it will be interesting to watch how the messaging evolves.

Monsanto: "Growing Better Together"
Who can argue with the goal of feeding more people using fewer natural resources? Monsanto has announced a commitment toward promoting the United Nations' Sustainable Development Goals. They especially focus on addressing water use, climate action, poverty, and hunger. But Monsanto is frequently maligned as an example of what is wrong with large-scale, commercial agriculture: overuse of pesticides, lack of crop diversity, and development of genetically modified organisms (GMOs). The company clearly has an uphill road in positioning itself as committed to environmental sustainability.

Scotts Miracle-Gro: "Help people of all ages express themselves on their own piece of the Earth"
That statement sounds innocuous enough. Still, the company has come under fire. Some have argued that its synthetic fertilizers and pesticides are creating environmental problems. Are customers' desires to express themselves through green lawns and flourishing plants worth it? Self-expression could perhaps be achieved just as well using native plants that don't require synthetic chemicals to grow well.

In the course of my research, I heard from representatives of some of the companies listed above. These people appear to truly believe that they work for companies that are trying to have a positive influence in the world. They believe that their employers have their customers' best interests at heart. I heard some compelling arguments.

Blue-green algae and agriculture

A story from Scotts Miracle-Gro illustrates the importance of transparency in communicating with customers, the challenge of distinguishing between perception and reality, and the difficulty that accompanies merely defending the science behind the story. It involves toxic algal blooms, a problem for which Scotts seems to have been unfairly blamed.

Toxic algal blooms are a serious threat to water quality in the Florida Everglades, Great Lakes, Chesapeake Bay, Puget Sound, and many waterways throughout the world. The source of these algal blooms? High levels of phosphorus in the water. Excess phosphorus creates an environment in which cyanobacteria, also known as blue-green algae, flourish. Cyanobacteria produce toxins that affect the human nervous system, liver, and skin.

In 2007, the Environmental Protection Agency (EPA) sampled water from 1,250 lakes in the US and found moderate to high levels of cyanobacteria (more than 20,000 cells/mL) in 315 of them. As a point of reference, algal blooms, where visible scum forms on the water surface, are associated with cyanobacteria levels of at least 100,000 cells/mL.

Scotts, as one of the largest manufacturers of fertilizers and pesticides in the US, became a target for environmental groups, who called them out as a chemical company producing phosphorus-laden products. Miracle-Gro is a product sold to homeowners, a group responsible for around 2 percent of fertilizer use in this country. Commercial agriculture is responsible for the bulk of phosphorus leaching into water supplies, but attacking farmers is not a popular position. Activists instead went after the chemical giants that sell fertilizers directly to consumers, even if the problem wasn't primarily their fault.

Jim King, communications officer for Scotts and president of the Scotts Miracle-Gro Foundation, says that the company's initial reaction to being attacked was to go on the defensive. It took the attitude of "we were right, and we knew it" based on the science behind the source of phosphorus contamination. But customers didn't want to hear about the science. Sales dropped.

Recognizing the need to address consumers' concerns, Scotts soon developed a phosphorus-free version of Miracle-Gro. They learned that naturally occurring levels of phosphorous in existing lawns are high enough that they could completely remove the element from their fertilizers while keeping them just as effective. While this begs the question of why the fertilizer contained phosphorus in the first place, the response does show that Scotts was listening to consumers.

Homeowners no longer routinely add phosphorus to their lawns. Of course, since household fertilizers were not the primary source of excessive phosphorous levels in lakes and rivers, toxic algal blooms have only increased in recent years. And although established lawns don't need phosphorus, newly seeded lawns will not thrive without both nitrogen and phosphorus. Still, removing phosphorus from their products showed customers that Scotts cared about their concerns and desire not to harm the environment.

King recognizes that educating consumers is difficult, especially when they are inundated with sensational news from multiple sources. It can be especially hard to convince consumers that the science is sound, so starting a discussion from the perspective of science is not usually the most effective approach.

The truth is complicated and confusing for consumers, most of whom don't have a background in chemistry and have probably forgotten whatever they might have learned about the subject in high school. The average consumer does not really understand how to best protect the environment. Employees tasked with product marketing are not in a much better position. They don't necessarily have any greater understanding of chemistry than the end user.

Company messaging needs to build trust by taking actions and being transparent about the process the company is undertaking to address a real or perceived environmental threat. Customers want a consistent message that they can understand. Scotts responded to this desire by sharing the whole story, including mistakes made along the way, to show customers that they have nothing to hide and respect customers' dual goals of having a beautiful yard and avoiding harming the environment.

Scotts has been working with multiple nongovernmental organizations (NGOs) whose mission it is to protect clean water. As a result, some of its harshest critics have become its advocates. The company formed the Scotts Miracle-Gro Foundation in February 2017 to expand and formalize its efforts to combat water pollution. Through a partnership with the Everglades Foundation, Scotts sponsors the George Barley Water Prize, a competition that will award $10 million to the group that comes up with the best scalable solution to remove phosphorus from fresh water. Scientists around the world, including more than one hundred teams from thirteen countries, are working on it.

Removing phosphorus from water is not an unsolvable problem, but to date no reasonably priced method exists. The hope is that the incentive of the Barley Prize will encourage the kind of ingenuity and innovation required to create a solution that is effective and scalable while raising awareness of the algal bloom problem. These types of partnerships between for-profit companies and NGOs can provide an alternative to consequences imposed in the form of added regulations.

Detecting toxins

Some elements and compounds have been proven toxic, and it is in everyone's best interest to limit exposure and dispose of waste in a properly controlled manner. Other compounds are suspected toxins, but the level of danger is not as well understood. Not everyone agrees on which compounds should be considered safe and what level of potentially dangerous ingredients or contaminants should be considered acceptable.

Advances in sensing are changing the landscape. Sensors too small to see now measure temperature, pressure, motion, and the presence of minute quantities of chemical substances. Sensors can detect the presence of solid, liquid, or gas molecules.

More sensitive measurements mean that toxins can be detected when contamination is low enough to measure in parts per billion or even parts per trillion. This creates a moving target for safe limits. Advances in measurement sensitivity make it harder for a company to argue that they didn't know that their product contained a certain toxin. Chemical analysis is readily available, and at a cost that can hardly be considered a barrier to knowledge.

Increased tracking makes it easier to evaluate a complete supply chain to determine where in a process a contaminant or substance of concern is finding its way in. This makes transparency less of a choice and more of a requirement. Despite the improved technology, however, supply chains are still very complicated. Multiple companies enter the picture from the point where materials are extracted from the Earth to the point where an end customer receives a product. Problems can still hide and remain undetected, especially if those causing the problems want them to remain hidden.

A story from a century ago illustrates this clearly. Even in the early twentieth century, when this story began, the ability to identify and measure a certain dangerous substance existed, as did evidence suggesting the serious-ness of the danger. Some people just didn't want to acknowledge it.

Radium, a supposed wonder material

The Radium Girls by Kate Moore, published in 2017, tells the story of the women and girls who worked for the United States Radium Corporation (USRC) in Orange, New Jersey, and the Radium Dial Company in Ottawa, Illinois. Business began booming for the USRC during World War I, with glow-in-the-dark watches headed to soldiers overseas. Even after the war, demand continued, and more companies sprung up as the radium industry grew. The Radium Dial Company was one of these.

News in those days didn't travel instantly, like it does today. When the USRC dial painters in New Jersey began falling ill and dying while still in their twenties, as a result of daily exposure to radium, the workers at the Radium Dial Company in Ottawa knew nothing about it. Girls and young women flocked to dial painting jobs at the new company for the money and the camaraderie, just as they had halfway across the country a decade earlier.

Day after day, they painted dials onto clocks and watches with glow-in-the-dark paint. The source of the glow? Radium, a naturally radioactive element. It seems shocking today, but a hundred years ago the company instructed the workers, many of whom were still in their teens, to lick the ends of their paint brushes to achieve the fine point necessary to paint details on miniature watch faces. The company told them it was perfectly safe. Safe? The girls were slowly poisoning themselves by ingesting small quantities of radium every day for years.

The disfigurement of these girls from radium poisoning and their pain-ful, drawn-out deaths is horrifying and sickening. Perhaps just as sickening is the attitude of the companies that employed the dial painters. Predictably, they denied responsibility for their employees' ailments despite mounting evidence to the contrary. They hired their own doctors and hid any evidence that suggested that the radium in the paint was linked to sickness or death.

USRC and Radium Dial Company may be considered as artifacts of the early twentieth century, a time supposedly before people understood the dangers of toxic materials. Although it seems hard to believe, radium was promoted as being good for the health. People actually drank tonics contain-ing tiny amounts of radium. But there were hints about the dangers as early as 1901. And Marie Curie, who earned a Nobel Prize for her discovery of radium, died from radium poisoning in 1934.

In *The Radium Girls*, the companies that were benefiting from selling radium products come across as being completely heartless, pursuing profits with no concern for the health of their employees. Kate Moore's book points out that the companies knew of the dangers of radium but hid it from workers, perhaps not unlike the attitude of the tobacco industry toward its customers decades later. Certainly, a corporation wouldn't dare lie to their workers, customers, or communities like this today, right? Unfortunately, some companies are still acting in ways that can only be described as reprehensible.

▨ Clean diesel? Sorry, but no

Volkswagen boasted a position on the Dow Jones Sustainability World Index in 2015, the year its emissions cheating scandal became international news. That year it had also been recognized as one of the most environmentally sustainable automobile manufacturers. Its cars, including some with diesel engines, won awards for being environmentally friendly. Unfortunately, a company can outwardly advertise its positive environmental impacts while hiding worse sins behind closed doors. I'll get to those sins in a moment.

The VW diesel scandal affected me personally. When the transmission went out on my 2001 Honda Odyssey, I was already tired of driving a minivan and looking for something smaller. Instead of putting thousands of dollars into repairing the Odyssey, I sold it for $1,700. The buyer was looking for a second car and knew someone who repaired transmissions. He probably only had to pay for the parts needed to install a new transmission and was able to return the car to a drivable condition. I'm all for reusing rather than dumping broken items, so it seemed like a win-win. Someone on a limited budget got a car for a good price, and I was no longer the owner of a non-running minivan.

I'm an analytical person. When it came to deciding which car to buy in 2011, I created a list of desired features and compared my top five cars. I chose the TDI diesel version of the VW Jetta Sportwagen. I looked back at my list in late 2016, shortly before selling my Jetta back to VW when the company offered a generous buyback program. The Jetta wasn't an obvious winner. What sold me, ironically, was the high fuel economy, along with the cargo space. I wasn't concerned about high fuel prices as much buying a car that was relatively environmentally friendly.

In retrospect, the VW was a poor choice. VW's so-called "clean diesel" was anything but clean. It seems hard to believe that engineers purposely installed software to cheat the system, but that's exactly what happened. During emissions tests, the cars passed with flying colors. They could even meet the tough California emission standards.

On the road, it was another story. My car, along with millions of others, emitted toxic nitrous oxides (NOx) at levels far above those deemed acceptable anywhere in the US. As Steven Howard says in his book *Leadership Lessons from the Volkswagen Saga*, VW engaged not in accidental negligence but "deliberate corporate malfeasance." In order to save just a few hundred dollars per car, they deliberately misled their customers, creating a health hazard and polluting the environment.

Steven Howard read more than 1,000 articles and court findings in researching his book about VW. He discovered that the decision came down to wanting to avoid a cost of $385 per vehicle to install a catalytic converter that would have reduced emissions to an acceptable level. The CEO didn't allow the cost increase and instead tasked the engineers with coming up with a different solution. In a culture where whistle-blowing wasn't an option, the engineers didn't have much of a choice. They had to "park their morals at the door."

In a strange twist, VW issued a recall of some of its TDI vehicles that were underperforming, some months after the emissions scandal had become public. It turns out that the cheat device software was responsible. Did VW admit what was happening? Absolutely not. It simply told customers to bring in their recalled vehicles for a free software upgrade. Without divulging the nature of the upgrade, they installed a new version of the cheat software that didn't interfere with vehicle performance. After the upgrade, the vehicles continued to emit just as much toxic NOx as before, only now the engine performance met consumer expectations.

The mysterious case of the ailing cattle

Corporate negligence is a more common occurrence. Companies continue to disregard evidence they don't want to see. Wilbur Tennant, a farmer in West Virginia whose cattle mysteriously began falling ill and dying, understands this all too well. Tennant knew there had to be a reasonable explanation for the problems on his farm. He suspected that a landfill near his property, owned by DuPont, was responsible.

Tennant found that no local politicians, doctors, or veterinarians would listen to his concerns. He contacted lawyer Rob Bilott and showed him graphic footage of what was happening to the cattle. Bilott took the case.

DuPont's response to Bilott's lawsuit was to commission a study, hiring its own veterinarians. They concluded, not surprisingly, that Tennant was delinquent in the care of his cattle, despite Tennant's evidence showing that the cattle had been healthy for decades. The problems started shortly after Tennant's brother sold land to DuPont and it built a landfill near Tennant's property.

Finally, compelled by court order, DuPont gave Bilott access to huge stacks of archived documents showing that the company knew for decades that it was discharging toxic chemicals into the landfill but had hidden all evidence.

The culprit was PFOA—perfluorooctanoic acid—which DuPont bought from 3M and used to produce Teflon and other products. DuPont's records specify that PFOA is to be disposed of in chemical waste facilities and never discharged into any bodies of water, but DuPont blatantly ignored their own guidelines.

PFOA, and a related compound, PFOS (perfluorooctane sulfonate), have been identified as biotoxins, poisons that accumulate in humans and animals and cause health problems. Medical studies on rats showed that PFOA is extremely damaging to internal organs. DuPont knew that PFOA was present in the local water supply, based on its own testing, but failed to disclose this detail.

The PFOA problem extends well beyond a single farm in West Virginia. A nonprofit organization conducted a survey and found that water supplies in twenty-seven states exceeds safe PFOA limits, as defined by researchers at Harvard and the University of Massachusetts. Did this happen decades ago? No. The survey results are from 2015.

Bilott filed a class action lawsuit against DuPont, which resulted in a $16.5 million settlement with the EPA, but this hardly puts a dent in DuPont's profits. Large companies can afford to pay millions of dollars to avoid further court battles and then go back to doing business as usual.

I am struck by some parallels in the stories of the Radium Dial Corporation and DuPont. The Radium Dial Corporation hired its own scientists to publish research claiming that radium was safe, even healthy. DuPont hired its own veterinarians to examine Tennant's farm.

My goal here is not to paint the companies I've mentioned as inherently evil. Their actions resulted in suffering, to be sure. When I learned about the DuPont story, my immediate reaction was to want to boycott the company. But that probably isn't the best approach. (I am, however, insistent that I will never again buy a VW car.)

I keep remembering a blog post that Mallen Baker wrote in 2016, called "Four reasons why you should never hate a company if you want to change the world." His premise was that an adversarial stance stands in the way of appreciating positive steps that the company is taking to remedy past actions.

Being adversarial isn't the best approach to convince the company to change its ways. Companies do change, as a result of internal or external pressures. With the US Environmental Protection Agency (EPA) working to dismantle many of the regulations that have led to cleaner air, water, and soil during my lifetime, it seems more important than ever to approach companies who are guilty of polluting with a message that is not going to put them on the defensive. As hard as it is to keep an open mind and try to learn all the facts, that's probably the best way to effect change.

Workplaces in the US are safer today than they were generations ago, in part because of the radium girls' story. Their lawsuits played a role in developing the Occupational Safety and Health Administration (OSHA), which protects workers in this country. Clearly, workplaces in the US are safer than they were in the early twentieth century. Labs, factories, and even products on store shelves are filled with warnings, and workers wear protective apparel when handling dangerous materials. Safety Data Sheets are mandatory. When radioactive materials or X-ray radiation are present, workers wear dosimeters to continually monitor their exposure levels.

Back to DuPont and its handling of PFOA. Finding replacements for toxic compounds is not a simple matter. In 2000, 3M announced that it would stop manufacturing PFOS. As recently as 2014, however, 3M customer Dow (now part of DuPont) was still working on finding alternative materials for some of its photoresists and antireflective coatings, materials that are used to produce patterned layers on the silicon chips that form the brains of electronic devices like cell phones and computers. The company had been gradually phasing out products that contained PFOA and PFOS but found it a daunting process.

Product information on Dow photoresists and coatings containing PFOA, published in 2014, warns about the solvents in these products. These liquid solvents, which evaporate when the photoresists and coatings are used in manufacturing, are "slightly to moderately toxic to aquatic organisms," according to Dow's product data sheets. The exposure risk occurs for workers handling the materials during manufacture of the chemicals and industrial use of them, though the risk can be minimized by following proper safety procedures. Communities surrounding manufacturing facilities become exposed to toxins if there is a leak or spill, or improper disposal, which is what happened in the DuPont case.

DuPont no longer produces these PFOA-containing materials that came from Dow, but it is important to understand that it took fifteen years of research and development to remove PFOA from the ingredient list. Without mandates from the EPA, the company may not have been willing to invest the time and money necessary to invent new versions of chemicals that were free of the offending compounds.

DuPont stands as an example of both the ways in which companies try to shirk responsibility and the challenges they face in replacing toxic materials with less toxic ones. Unlike USRC and the Radium Dial Corporation, whose entire line of business depended on promoting the safety and usefulness of radium, DuPont makes a vast range of products from many different chemical compounds. Business could go on without PFOA.

The pollution of water supplies around the country, even in regions where no known illicit dumping had occurred, suggested that it would be prudent to remove PFOA entirely. But DuPont had customers to satisfy and it wasn't willing to suddenly pull its products out of circulation.

DuPont has taken actions that have had a positive impact over the past couple of decades. It is important to distinguish between companies that are purposely hiding evidence of potential wrongdoing and those who have been put into a difficult position. Compounds that happen to be hazardous add useful functions to the products they are producing. Yes, their position is partly of their own making. DuPont was complicit in the chemical industry's long history of ignoring health and safety hazards in favor of performance advantages.

There are various factors to examine when considering DuPont's record. For example, DowDuPont is listed in the Dow Jones Sustainability World Index, which suggests that the company is indeed working toward being a good corporate citizen. But VW also earned a place on that list. The Ethisphere Institute named DuPont CEO Ed Breen as one of the one hundred most influential people in business ethics in 2009, which suggests that he values ethical behavior. But I noticed that he hasn't landed on the list since.

Beholden to shareholders

Today's capitalism is heavily weighted toward satisfying shareholders, sometimes at the expense of other considerations. It should be possible for a company to make money without endangering its employees or customers, but when profit is king, the vision can be too narrowly focused on the stock price.

As an investor in mutual funds, I am perhaps complicit. I have been a customer of Vanguard since the late 1990s. In an effort to better align my investments with my values, I chose to direct the Individual 401(k) for my business to Vanguard's Social Index Fund. I realize that there are investment companies solely devoted to socially conscious investing, which might have been better choices, but I admit that I instead took the easier path.

Vanguard's Social Index Fund invests according to the FTSE4Good US Select Index. That index screens its investments based on certain social, human rights, and environmental criteria. Its investments are heavily slanted toward financial and technology sectors, with health care not far behind. The fund bans certain industries, such as tobacco, but does include exposure to the oil and gas industry.

Some people argue that it is impossible to include oil and gas stocks in a socially responsible investing platform, but the reality is that society today relies on this industry to power our cities. Citizens still demand electricity and fuel, so the entire blame cannot be placed on the companies that provide this resource. Energy companies that produce fossil fuels while also promoting increased proportions of renewable energy may be worth supporting as being the best within their industry class. Oil and gas make up only 3 percent of the Social Index Fund's holdings.

In the basic materials category, which makes up less than 2 percent of its total investments, the Social Index Fund invests in the Newmont Mining Corporation. Mining, covered more extensively in Chapter 5, is dangerous, dirty work. It harms people and the environment. If all mining were to suddenly cease, however, the world would face a real shortage of resources. Therefore, at present mining can be considered a necessary evil, and supporting mining companies that are "less bad" than others seems a reasonable compromise that might encourage the worst offenders to change their ways.

Newmont seems to meet that criterion. The company operates gold mines in the US, Australia, Ghana, and Peru and claims to be committed to "sustainable and responsible mining." In 2018, the American Institute of Mining, Metallurgical, and Petroleum Engineers awarded Newmont CEO Gary Goldberg an award for his contributions to improving safety and sustainability in the mining industry. The Dow Jones Sustainability World Index named Newmont the mining industry leader in overall sustainability in 2015, 2016, and 2017.

The four system conditions

The word "sustainable" has been used to describe various aspects of doing business. The focus in this book is on how decisions regarding materials and manufacturing processes contribute to environmental sustainability. Removing known toxins, chemicals associated with endangering public health, is a big piece of that effort. But the effort goes beyond simply removing toxins.

The concept of "four system conditions" embraces a comprehensive but practical approach, recognizing the need to avoid increasing certain undesirable practices. Eliminating such practices entirely is a laudable but probably unachievable goal. The Natural Step, a multinational nonprofit with a mission to "accelerate the transition to a sustainable society," has reworded the four system conditions in terms of four principles:

1. Eliminate systematic increases in the amount of material extracted from the Earth.

2. Eliminate systematic increases in production of toxic substances of concern.

3. Avoid systematic increases in destruction of natural resources.

4. Avoid practices that contribute to undermining people's ability to meet their basic needs or create unsafe working conditions.

The Natural Step recognizes that materials will still need to be extracted from the Earth in the foreseeable future, and that the chemical industry is not disappearing. Their goal focuses on shrinking the rate at which resources are being used by considering where materials come from and how they are being extracted and processed. They advocate changes such as substituting less energy-intensive or less toxic materials. The Natural Step works with both local governments and businesses large and small, including such giants as Nike, which adopted their approach back in 1998.

Nike worked with The Natural Step from 1998 to 2001 and then again in 2008. By 2008, Nike had already addressed problems related to treatment of workers who were manufacturing its products overseas. It was no longer being accused of labor violations, and it had already made strides in reducing toxins. Nike began phasing out polyvinyl chloride (PVC) from its products in 1999 and had started buying organic cotton to avoid the high levels of pesticides used to grow conventional cotton. The company had replaced petroleum-based adhesives and cleaners with water-based products. These steps created safer working conditions and an environmental benefit.

But Nike wanted to expand its environmentally sound production practices and make sustainability central to its core mission. Reducing a toxin by 90 percent is admirable, but removing it entirely is much better. In partnership with The Natural Step, Nike developed a long-term vision called the North Star that set concrete, challenging goals such as designing all products to consider closed-loop materials usage.

Instead of materials being extracted, processed, made into products, and then discarded, a closed loop reclaims materials from products that are no longer useful and puts them back into a manufacturing cycle. Part III delves more deeply into this concept and the more comprehensive idea of the circular economy, where ideally materials never become trash.

Nike has collected used shoes for many years, grinding up the soles to make athletic fields and tracks. The North Star goals push the company to go further, starting from the design step. As William McDonough and Michael Braungart emphasized in their ground-breaking book *Cradle to Cradle*, good design is central to wise use of natural and synthetic materials.

As the Nike example shows, a thorough evaluation of the four system conditions requires digging beneath the surface. This involves investigating what is happening upstream and downstream, beyond a company's own manufacturing facilities.

For example, companies should look at not only what materials they extract from the Earth, and in what quantities, but where the materials come from. For example, does the company avoid using conflict minerals, those mined from war-torn regions of the world where workers are subjected to horrifying conditions?

Toxic substances of concern pose a difficult challenge. Getting rid of environmental toxins is much harder than simply reducing exposure. A level of zero is impossible to measure, even with today's advanced sensors. Getting below detectable limits is the best to hope for.

If a company is absolutely dedicated to removing toxins, and top executives are behind the effort, it can happen. Companies still need to invest time and money to even determine which toxins various products contain. They must trace everything back to suppliers, and suppliers' suppliers. If products contain recycled materials, those materials sometimes include unintended toxic contaminants, as we will see in Chapter 6. Recycling isn't without risks.

Sourcing wood or palm oil from sustainably managed forests, where more trees are planted than harvested and clear cutting is usually avoided, reduces the destruction of natural resources. Not all mining operations are equally destructive. It is also possible to reduce the quantity of mined metals a company is using to begin with, through substituting recycled metals or making design changes.

Increasingly, environmental sustainability is being linked with social justice. It is more just to produce environmentally friendly products that average citizens can afford, and also to consider the conditions under which those products are being made. Worker safety cannot be ignored. Environmentally oriented industry conferences are including a much greater emphasis on social justice, sometimes devoting entire sessions to the topic.

INTERVIEW   Mallen Baker, CSR Consultant

Mallen Baker believes that it is important to distinguish between companies that are genuinely interested in moving beyond major mistakes and improving their environmental stance and those who continue to willfully disregard safety in order to focus on short-term profits. I tend to agree with him.

Mallen comes to his role as a corporate social responsibility (CSR) consultant and blogger on CSR from a background in local politics. He served for a year as principal speaker of the Green Party of England.

Through his experience with Business in the Community, a membership organization for socially responsible business in the UK, Mallen learned about the importance of the attitudes of key executives in a company. The leadership must stand behind making sustainability part of the company mission, or efforts by individual employees will go nowhere. Mallen wishes that the CSR community would put a greater focus on looking into the beliefs and actions of CEOs.

In Mallen's view it makes sense that companies should be driven by a long-term view. They ought to prefer to create products that don't poison their customers or communities, so long as they can do so and still turn a profit. NGOs who have legitimate complaints about a company's practices would be better served by believing that, if informed about the risks of what it is doing, the company will be open to change. Assuming that the company is evil and will never change its ways is not productive. Boycotts get attention from the press and the public, but boycotting a company's products will likely not make the company go out of business. A cooperative stance, while putting pressure where it is deserved, is more likely to lead to improved conditions for workers or reduced hazardous emissions. NGOs can better make their voices heard if they recognize when companies make progress toward the goals that the NGO is trying to promote.

When an organization such as Greenpeace uses aggressive tactics against a company, that can be a great opportunity for organizations like Business in the Community. Businesses under attack don't want to let Greenpeace in their doors, but they will open them to an organization that seems more business-friendly. The attack serves as a wake-up call for the need to take action before news of the company's transgressions leads to declining sales. With the right type of education, from entities that they trust, companies can indeed change their direction and incorporate more environmentally friendly practices into their mission.

CHAPTER 3

Reining in Excess Waste

*"When we blame the person, that stops us from
actually getting to the root cause of the problem.
A lean culture is one that is open to admitting fault."*

—Kjell van Zoen, Lean Consultant

"It's cheaper than it should be to throw things away."

—Brion Hurley, Lean Consultant

Considering material consumption

Manufacturing requires a huge quantity of raw materials. The drive for greater wealth throughout the world has led to greater consumption of material goods. Common wisdom says that to remain healthy, an economy has to grow at a certain percentage a year, and that requires producing more and more things to sell to a growing population. While the economy also grows by selling services, the measure of wealth in a country is in a large part related to how much stuff the average person owns.

The book *Material World: A Global Family Portrait* by Peter Menzel and Charles Mann shows the stark contrast in wealth around the world through photographs of the "average" family in thirty countries, surrounded by all their possessions. Families literally emptied out their houses to create the photographs.

This book was published in 1995, before Western-style material consumption had spread to more rural nations and before consumer electronics had become ubiquitous. The US family in the book owned several cars and lots of furniture but only one computer. It would be interesting to see what a similar book would look like today.

Per capita materials usage in the US grew more than six-fold during the twentieth century. These calculations of material consumption don't even account for the materials in imported goods. Much of this increase is a result of the growth in size of homes in this country, from an average of 1,000 square feet in 1900 to 2,500 square feet in 2005.

I have to admit that I am part of the problem. When my husband and I bought our current house in 2014, our real estate agent pressured us into buying a larger home than our family needed. Since we had the luxury of a significant budget, having sold our home in the San Francisco Bay Area for an obscenely high sum, the assumption was that we needed to buy a certain level of luxury. In the Seattle area, price per square foot is significantly lower, compelling us to buy a home with a three-car garage and a guest bedroom. It's nice, but was it really necessary? Our home in California was large enough.

Europe has done a better job than the US in constraining excess consumption and reducing waste. This is in a large part thanks to greater overall population density and more efficient transportation systems. Cars and homes are generally smaller in Europe, and per capita materials usage has declined in

Tons of materials extracted per person, per year

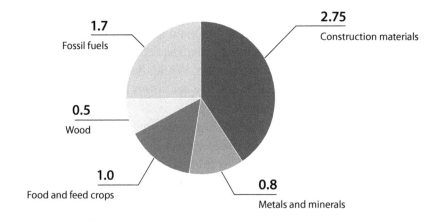

1.7 Fossil fuels

2.75 Construction materials

0.5 Wood

1.0 Food and feed crops

0.8 Metals and minerals

Data from Vaclav Smil, *Making the Modern World*

some European countries in the past decade. Rising materials usage in parts of Asia, Latin America, and Africa, however, more than makes up for it. The global trend remains one of increased production of materials and goods.

Vaclav Smil, in his book *Making the Modern World*, calculated the quantity of resources grown or extracted per person on Earth in a year (see pie chart). Most the resources are used to make engineered materials—metals from mineral ores, plastics from fossil fuels, and construction materials such as concrete, brick, and tile—as well as providing the fuels needed for transportation, heating, and electricity.

Reducing these quantities remains a good idea, but perhaps not for the reasons that some people think. The real problem of resource extraction is not that the world is going to run out of resources. Extraction causes pollution and damage to the land around a mine, as well as emitting greenhouse gases that contribute to climate change. Without delving into the science behind climate change here, suffice it to say that climate change is a real problem, and materials usage can play a role in shrinking that impact.

Are we really running out?

People sometimes promote recycling as a solution to the risk of running out of natural resources. This concern pertains not only to water but to production of both plastics, which today rely on fossil fuels, and metals, which rely on ores. (For more about these materials, see Part II). It can be difficult to tell whether this idea of resource scarcity is a real or perceived risk.

In the case of water, local scarcity is a real problem, exacerbated by droughts and floods that are more severe than ever. For Cape Town, South Africa, 2017–2018 marked the third straight season of severe drought. When combined with a growing population, the drought presented a huge problem. As of early 2018, the city of four million was on the verge of running out of water before the rainy season started in June or July. In January, city officials estimated that reservoirs held only ninety days' worth of water. The city barely avoided "day zero," defined as the day when municipal water taps are shut off, which was originally planned to occur in April. Doing so required extreme conservation measures. Residents lined up for hours to fill containers from natural springs and rationed those containers carefully.

Fossil fuels and mineral ores do not present the same level of resource scarcity risk as do water supplies. Predictions of "peak oil," when oil and gas reserves were going to start a downward trend early in the twenty-first century, have not come to pass. When supplies of certain ores have reached diminishing returns, new mining locations have been found.

Part of the challenge is in distinguishing between the existence of potential new sources of resources on Earth and the expense—in both money and harm to the environment—of extracting them. If the expense to extract the wealth within specific sources of fuel or materials is prohibitive, then the source might as well not exist as far as commercial extraction is concerned. The environmental impact of newer technologies such as hydraulic fracturing of rocks to extract the resources inside them—better known as fracking—is another concern.

It is also important to distinguish between reserves and resources. The supply of any specific resource—the total mass of material located within the Earth's crust—is unknown. The estimate is a moving target that changes every time exploration reveals a new possible source. Even if we knew the total quantity of a resource, it would not be feasible to extract it all. Minerals that exist deep underground or in extremely small concentrations at a specific location cannot be extracted at a cost that makes it worth the expense of extracting them.

Reserves stand as the more important measurement. The quantity of material in reserve represents the share of a resource that can be extracted using existing techniques and at an acceptable cost. The value changes over time but is well-defined and considered to be accurate.

By comparing annual production needs to the amount of a mineral in reserve, it is possible to calculate the number of years the supply will last. Some alarmists use these calculations to suggest that the Earth is at risk of running out of some mineral or another, but the reality is that the mining industry is continually finding new sources and developing better techniques for extracting the minerals within them.

As an example, the ratio of reserves to annual production of copper was 42.8 years in 2011. This does not mean that the Earth will run out of copper within my lifetime, or within my children's lifetime. This ratio was about the same in 1980. According to Smil, who has studied historical data in excruciating detail, there is no risk that society will run out of any common metals in the next sixty or eighty years.

Smil was not considering the specialty metals used in minute quantities in cell phones. Still, these are probably not in danger of disappearing from the Earth either. Plenty of ores containing these metals exist in the Earth's crust. The problem lies in the feasibility of extracting enough of them within time lines that device manufacturers demand, and at a price they are willing to pay. When considered from this viewpoint, there exists a real risk of supply shortages.

Consider the time horizon between discovering a new location where a mine could be constructed and mining the minerals within it: between ten and fifteen years from initial exploration to productive mining. This is quite a long time compared to the production cycles of consumer electronics. When a potential mine is located in a country with an unstable government, this adds to the risk and complicates the challenge of extracting and distributing the minerals.

There are clearly uncertainties surrounding availability of resources. A 2017 article in *Nature* warned about challenges in maintaining sufficient mineral supplies to satisfy society's increasing demand for technology, especially as such demand extends to regions of the world that are relatively unconnected today and the number of devices in circulation worldwide skyrockets. Author Saleem Ali pointed out the demand for large quantities of many different minerals and suggested that recycling will not be sufficient to ensure availability.

I'm not convinced that that is the case, given new e-waste recycling capabilities being developed (see Chapter 7), but his point about the importance of managing the global mineral supply seems valid. He proposes coming up with international agreements to ensure stable prices for minerals needed for technology-related applications. These minerals are sold through individual dealers, rather than a global commodities market, which tends to make prices fluctuate widely.

▣ The challenge of reducing materials usage

Reducing the global extraction of raw materials is a noble goal, but an extremely difficult one. As manufacturing efficiency improves, similar products can be made with lower consumption of energy or materials and therefore at lower cost. As a direct result, the total number of products produced tends to increase. Mass ownership promotes greater consumption.

The cell phone provides a perfect example. It is possible to look at the cell phone as replacing many objects that used to be commonplace in everyday use: a traditional corded phone, alarm clock, camera, map, and address book. The weight of all these products is several kilograms (several thousand grams), compared to not much more than 100 grams for a smart phone. Cell phones themselves have shrunk in weight since they first became popular in the 1990s.

But the vast quantity of cell phones being produced more than makes up for any supposed savings. Approximately eleven million cell phones were produced in 1990, with an average weight of 600 grams. Around 1.5 billion cell phones are now produced and sold every year.

If reducing the total amount of global resource consumption is not realistic, what then? One avenue involves reaching an easier goal of reducing the waste generated per product. This approach is a good starting point, although the ideal of reducing total resource consumption should be kept in mind. Absolute reduction better aligns with the four system conditions, discussed in Chapter 2.

Sometimes moves that would seem to obviously reduce material consumption do not necessarily do so. As one example, the trend toward electronic rather than paper copies of documents certainly reduces the number of trees that need to be cut down to produce paper. What is often left out of the story, though, are the resources required to produce the computing power that enables electronic document generation and transfer.

The internet is not resource-neutral. Banks of servers, built with raw materials, are required to manage all that global data flow. Huge quantities of energy are needed to run the data centers and cool the buildings to keep servers from overheating. Big data requires big resources.

The focus in this book, however, is on the materials required to produce tangible products. Companies involved in manufacturing have already made many changes that enable them to produce more goods using fewer and less toxic resources.

Creating lighter, more efficient computers, vehicles, and airplanes has been accomplished in part by replacing steel and glass with aluminum and plastics. As we will see in Chapter 6, these lighter materials require much more energy to produce per ton of end product. This doesn't mean that such substitutions are a bad idea, however. The products do require lower weights of materials, so the energy of materials production may balance out. Without doing the calculations, however, it isn't clear that replacing materials has the level of positive effect that designers intended. Weight is not the only aspect that needs to be considered.

▓ Moving toward zero waste

Reducing global materials consumption by a significant amount requires a shift in mindset away from the buy-consume-discard approach. Efforts need to go beyond nominal increases in rates of recycling. Businesses and their customers need to consider each product as part of a bigger picture. What materials are used to make the product, and how were they produced? How long can the product itself be used? Is there a resale market for the product? What happens to the product once it has outlived its usefulness as originally intended?

The idea of shifting from a linear economy to a circular one is not new. William McDonough and Michael Braungart published *Cradle to Cradle* back in 2002. Instead of products moving from cradle to grave, they find continual use. Biobased or organic materials—anything that can decompose or biodegrade—return to the earth in a continuous cycle. They enrich the soil, much like wastes from plants and animals have done for millennia. Inorganic materials become part of a technical cycle, ground up and melted to produce materials for the next generation of engineered products.

It appears that this shift to a circular economy is the answer to managing nonrenewable resources. Businesses—especially large businesses producing millions or billions of products every year—have the clout to insist that such a shift take place. On the flip side, companies also have the ability to put the brakes on attempts to change and continue the status quo while appearing to take positive action.

What level of responsibility is the business community willing to take on? The level appears to be growing as more businesses publicly announce commitments to addressing their roles in polluting the environment and creating mountains of waste.

Merely an intent to save resources is of course not enough. The trick is to accurately measure resource usage and track progress toward concrete goals. Saving resources often leads to saving money. Without tracking exactly how much they are spending on electricity, water, or waste disposal, however, a company won't know the best places to look for cost savings. Sustainability reporting (see Chapter 9) requires companies to gather such data. Each year, more companies are jumping on board to create industry-standard reports.

It isn't possible for a business to produce zero waste, but it can create zero waste to landfill. The methods for achieving this goal matter. Ideally, zero-waste-to-landfill programs reduce the total quantity of materials needed to make products and reuse more resources on-site while considering the overall environmental impact of any changes. The alternative, burning excess waste to avoid sending it to a landfill, likely increases energy use and releases toxic fumes into the environment.

Most people understand that zero-waste-to-landfill programs are not just good for the environment, they are good for the bottom line. Some

g facilities filter wastewater at their production plant and recy-
into the system. The water bill goes down and the facility doesn't
to pay for permits to release wastewater. Machine shops collect metal
scraps and remelt them to make more products. Making more products with
the same quantity of incoming metal is more efficient and saves money. The
manufacturing process also creates less solid waste, reducing waste disposal
costs.

Brewer Science, based in Rolla, Missouri, stands as an example. It produces
chemicals and materials used to make computer chips. This is a resource-
intensive industry, and one that can be extremely toxic. Brewer achieved its
goal of zero waste to landfill in 2015. At the same time, the company significantly reduced its usage of water, electricity, and natural gas from 2010
to 2015. The achievement required a commitment from the entire company. They needed to upgrade equipment, improve data collection, conduct
employee training, and collaborate with suppliers and customers. As a result,
employees at all levels feel responsible for doing their part to keep the system
on track.

INTERVIEW Kjell van Zoen and Brion Hurley, Lean Consultants

I met Kjell van Zoen and Brion Hurley at the GoGreen Portland conference
in October 2017. They led a session on "lean," the manufacturing principles
that Toyota has been espousing for decades. Companies typically adopt
lean to make manufacturing more efficient and reduce wasted time and
expenses. Reducing toxins and working toward zero-waste-to-landfill
goals tie very nicely into lean methodology.

Controlling inventory translates to storing less material to begin with. By
keeping a tight lid on the quantity of raw materials being ordered, it is
possible to manage multiple sources of waste. Implementing just-in-time
manufacturing—producing parts or products as customers request them
or the next step in the manufacturing process needs them—delays the
need to extract new materials from the Earth. In the case of trees, this
allows them to grow taller and stronger and spend more time doing their
part to absorb carbon dioxide from the atmosphere. The concept is also
beneficial when considering industrial materials such as metal ores and
feedstock for plastics. Less raw material extracted translates to less energy
consumed and lower levels of toxins generated.

Reducing inventory also avoids the waste involved in discarding excess materials or goods. Materials or goods that can no longer be made into products or sold to customers because the bill of materials or product specifications have changed become a waste stream. Some excess materials are recyclable, but it is better not to have produced them in the first place.

Brion:

Brion came from the world of lean and Six Sigma and hadn't thought much about environmental sustainability early in his career. A statistics major in college, his background was in data analysis. Brion started his career as a statistician and quality engineer at an aerospace firm, Rockwell Collins. In that role, he combined lean and Six Sigma, an approach to eliminating manufacturing defects.

As Brion learned about the problem of climate change and carbon footprint, he realized that lean practices could help businesses reduce their energy use and toxic waste disposal. Brion moved back to his hometown and took sustainability training at the University of Iowa in 2009 to give him the tools he needed to help form a green team at Rockwell Collins. That program never took off, however, because the executive team wasn't heavily enough invested in the concept. Like many companies at the time, Rockwell Collins wasn't ready for Brion's message.

Despite Brion's challenges in forming a green team, he did help Rockwell Collins reduce waste. Brion shared an example in which Rockwell Collins was receiving parts from a supplier that were over-packaged. The excess packaging was not only wasteful in terms of materials that could not be recycled. Staff was having to take a lot of time to remove the packaging, which included many layers of tape, to use the parts in Rockwell Collins's own manufacturing process.

By working with the parts supplier, they were able to transition some parts to being protected with custom reusable packaging. It did cost money to ship empty packaging crates back to the supplier, but that also served as a sign for the supplier that its customer needed more parts. Rather than sticking to a fixed delivery schedule, the supplier knew to ship more parts only when they received an empty box. Now the supplier wasn't producing parts until they were needed, and Rockwell Collins wasn't storing the parts while waiting for some other aspect of their production process to be ready.

Reusable packaging isn't always the best option. Delicate parts that come in many different shapes and sizes may not be properly protected with a one-size-fits-many approach. In this case, reusable packaging isn't efficient, especially if it leads to parts becoming damaged and unusable. For these types of parts, Rockwell Collins's supplier was still able to use less disposable packaging per item.

At one point, Brion transferred to a Rockwell Collins facility near Portland, Oregon. Even in the more pro-environment culture of the Pacific Northwest, he realized that he needed to strike out on his own to make a greater impact. In his view, change needed to be greater than merely switching out light bulbs. He was inspired by the possibility of helping companies make a business case for positive environmental actions.

Brion started his consulting practice in 2017 with the goal of either teaching sustainability professionals about lean, or teaching lean or Six Sigma professionals about environmental sustainability. In his experience, the first method has gained more followers.

His approach starts with the idea of cutting out waste and inefficiency, the core of lean, and then tries to tie it to environmental benefit. Sometimes implementing sustainability practices accidentally leads to an improvement in manufacturing processes, as was the case with the Rockwell Collins example.

In his fledgling consulting practice, Brion works with several nonprofits, including the ReBuilding Center and Free Geek in Portland, that are already focused on sustainability. He has been working with a team of volunteers to teach these organizations about lean.

The ReBuilding Center acts as a clearinghouse for used construction materials. People donate a wide variety of still usable supplies and the ReBuilding Center sells them to customers looking to saving money and resources while remodeling. A snapshot of incoming items received on a single day included iron bench railings, concrete posts, interior doors, lumber, bricks, and crystal chandeliers.

The ReBuilding Center wanted to understand which of its materials were selling and which were sitting on the shelves, in order to better organize its warehouse and price materials appropriately. Brion recommended that the ReBuilding Center better track their inventory over time to figure out which materials weren't attracting customers. The ReBuilding Center would then be in a position to decide which materials to no longer accept because those materials are just taking up space and not fulfilling their intended purpose.

Although tracking inventory seems to be an obvious solution, the reality is that the company had no way of tracking it other than relying on worker memory. A desire to advance the organization's mission also hampered efforts to reduce inventory—workers felt conflicted about removing inventory from the floor to dispose of or recycle the item, since their overall goal is to keep items in circulation.

Free Geek is addressing the e-waste problem by collecting electronics, refurbishing them, and donating them to individuals and organizations in need. For donated items too old or damaged to be refurbished, Free Geek sends them to certified responsible e-waste recyclers in Japan. Certification is not a guarantee that electronics will be recycled properly, but it is at least a step in the right direction.

Free Geek often has a backlog of laptops awaiting refurbishing and distribution. Brion has been working with them to make their processes more efficient, allowing them to get more products out into the community faster with the same number of staff and volunteers.

Brion's next wave of clients includes those who need improvements in implementing both lean and sustainability. He believes that contests and competitions within organizations can be very effective in encouraging employees to be engaged in making a safer workplace and creating safer products. A statistician at heart, Brion also believes in the power of data to convince people how a change in practices will affect their business. What gets measured gets people's attention.

Brion has gotten behind ISO 26000, a guideline that addresses social responsibility. Environment is one of seven subjects covered, as is corporate governance. Employees will be more likely to bring up potential problems if they believe that their management and the executive team will support them, rather than call them out for being whistle-blowers. The guideline also talks about whether decisions at the corporate level are driven by data or by instinct. Are employees being treated fairly and

g paid fair wages? What about the employees at a company's suppli-
/ Brion believes that lean and Six Sigma can help with all these issues.

Kjell:

A serial entrepreneur, Kjell first became involved with lean practices when
he ran a manufacturing firm, Plywerk. He sold Plywerk, which creates
photos mounted on custom recycled wood blocks, to a competitor in
2016. The brand remains, true to its legacy of sustainable manufacturing,
but with expanded offerings from the new owners.

Kjell then ran his own consulting business, VanZoen LLC, where he advised
small businesses on lean practices. He worked mostly with small organizations, those with 100 to 500 employees. Kjell now works as a strategic
energy management coach for Energy 350, Inc. helping large manufacturing clients reduce their energy needs through continuous improvement methodologies. He also runs training sessions and seminars for
Lean Portland Benefit LLC.

Kjell sees lean as controlling the flow of four things—information, materials,
people's time and energy, and cash—to improve efficiency. Lean focuses
on both investing in people and reducing the use of materials. Some assets,
such as resources owned by a business and required for its operation, are
beneficial. Others, such as inventory, are burdens. Kjell asks companies to
define material inventory guidelines that allow them to create the minimum number products to meet customer demand, but no more.

Lean isn't necessarily tied to circular economy principles, but it could be.
Companies can apply lean principles to considering what happens to
its products at the end of life. Take-back programs—such as Patagonia
repairing clothing or HP recycling inkjet cartridges—accomplish a version of this. But if doing so won't save a company money or time, it isn't
necessary to incorporate circular economy practices into lean.

Still, the circular economy can be considered as pushing the boundaries
of lean. Lean practices are usually focused only on what happens within
an organization, starting from buying materials and ending with shipping
products. Lean can expand to consider what happens from the time raw
materials are extracted to the time products are landfilled, recycled, or
composted. Kjell appreciates how the whole-systems-thinking that lean
embodies can be applied on a greater scale.

At one point, Plywerk evaluated its entire manufacturing process using the four system conditions principles. Kjell and his business partner measured all the materials used in their operations—wood, adhesives, packaging materials, etc.—and ranked each material based on how it related to the system conditions and how often they used it in their manufacturing processes. They discovered that the bubble wrap used to package its products was the greatest offender in terms of environmental impact. They replaced bubble wrap with a padded paper product called Geami. That simple change avoided the production of 40,000 square feet of bubble wrap per year without changing packaging costs.

Kjell told me the story of one of his clients who had a problem with filing cabinets. This client owned four massive filing cabinets filled with products—cases for phones and laptops—representing hundreds of thousands of dollars' worth of inventory. The client produced hundreds of different versions of its products for various sized electronics and had a policy of shipping within a day of receiving a customer order. The inventory kept growing, and when Kjell started working with them, the company was considering expanding into another facility to manage everything.

Kjell convinced his client that keeping an inventory of products designed for older devices just in case a customer ordered one was not efficient. They incorporated just-in-time manufacturing, running only part of their production process in advance and customizing products as customers placed orders.

Within a year, they had gotten rid of the filing cabinets and closed one building. They were using less energy, lower quantities of materials, and saving money on rent. The client accomplished this while selling more products than ever before.

Applying the lean concept to cell phones, Kjell suggests that the most efficient model would have one company in each geographic region selling phones to its local market. No individual would need to own more than one phone, and they would keep this phone for much longer before replacing it. The phones would be standardized to avoid the need to store inventory of multiple different versions. But in such a world, innovation would take a back seat and customers would have fewer choices, which would not make the approach very popular with manufacturers or consumers.

Lean practices ideally shouldn't squelch innovation. But environmental sustainability and lean aren't necessarily connected if the environmental piece isn't a priority for the company. Lean doesn't require zero waste to landfill, for example, even though the practice is compatible with lean. If a company that is devoted to lean prioritizes environmentally friendly manufacturing, however, it had better follow through in practice. Greenwashing would conflict with the principles of lean. As Kjell sees it, lean is about being honest with yourself and presenting your company in a way that is consistent with its stated mission and vision.

PART II

The Materials We Use

CHAPTER 4

Plastics—Wonder Materials or Global Disaster?

"Plant-based packaging has the potential to grow to 10, 20, 30 percent of the disposable packaging market and beyond as consumer preferences and pressures change over time."
—Mark Stephany, World Centric

"No one wants to use petroleum, but if that's all that's out there, what can you do?"
—Sam Hopkins, EcoSheep

Plastics are everywhere

Plastics have become ubiquitous in modern civilization. Despite families in the developed world pledging to go a week or a month without buying any plastic and succeeding in this endeavor, those same families could not have separated themselves completely from the plastic they already own. As Susan Freinkel demonstrated in the introduction to her book *Plastic: A Toxic Love Story*, her attempt to avoid touching plastics for a day immediately evolved into tracking her interaction with plastics. She discovered that she touched nearly 200 different plastic objects in a single day.

The website of the International Association of Plastics Distribution (IAPD) states, "There is absolutely no way you could or would want to go a day without interacting in some way with performance plastic." The IAPD was founded in 1956, with the goal of helping member companies build their businesses. Although the IAPD is biased toward plastics, the organization is right about the dominance of plastics in our society. IAPD also recognizes the need to address environmental sustainability, an aspect that features prominently in their marketing.

Plastics can appear to be an ideal replacement for wood, metal, or glass, depending on the application. They are inexpensive, lightweight, and durable. When accidentally dropped, most plastic objects neither break nor damage the surface onto which they fall. Plastic can be easily formed into complex shapes using a variety of manufacturing methods. It can be injection molded, in which molten plastic is injected into a metal mold and quickly solidifies upon contact with the cold metal. Plastic is soft enough to be easily machined.

Some plastic materials are transparent to light, making them an inexpensive substitute for glass. Toughened glass—the glass used in car windshields and bulletproof windows—includes one or more layers of plastic sandwiched between panes of glass. These composite materials combine the shatter-resistance of plastic with the scratch-resistance of glass.

It is possible to infuse plastics with opaque color. Unlike with painted objects, the color does not rub off the surface during use. This feature is great for manufacturers wanting to produce long-lasting products in a wide variety of colors. LEGO bricks come to mind as an obvious example.

Plastics have clearly become an indispensable part of modern society. For better or worse, it is difficult to imagine any industrialized nation without plastics. But there are those who see plastics as an evil to be eradicated. This chapter delves into both the positive and negative attributes of plastics, answering questions that many people ask about plastics:

- What are plastics and how are they made?
- When were plastics invented?
- How are different plastics used?
- Which plastics are toxic?
- How much of a problem is plastic trash?
- How can society reduce the use of plastics?
- What are bioplastics and how can they help?

What are plastics?

Everyone is familiar with plastics, but what are they really, and how are they made? A definition from *Webster's New Collegiate Dictionary (1975)* provides some insight:

Plastic (adj): capable of being molded; capable of being deformed continuously and permanently in any direction without rupture; of, relating to, or involving plastic surgery; artificial or synthetic.

Plastic (noun): a plastic substance; any of numerous organic synthetic or processed materials that are mostly thermoplastic or thermosetting polymers of high molecular weight and that can be molded, cast, extruded, drawn, or laminated into objects, films, or filaments.

In the context of plastic materials, "organic" means composed of hydrocarbons, molecules of carbon and hydrogen atoms that are the basis of life on Earth. All living things contain these molecules, which are classified based on how many carbon atoms they contain.

Polymers consist of long chains of hydrocarbons linked together to form large molecules. Polymers do exist in nature. Cellulose, a fiber found in trees and other plants, is a naturally occurring polymer. Spider silk is also a polymer, one with an impressive strength-to-weight ratio that engineered materials struggle to achieve. Such biopolymers serve as an inspiration for the field of biomimicry, in which chemists and engineers endeavor to create manufactured materials that mimic the properties of these perfectly designed natural materials. Plastics, however, are not naturally occurring or living materials, hence the phrase "synthetic or processed."

Commercial polymers include polypropylene, polyethylene, polyvinyl chloride (PVC), and polystyrene, also known by the familiar trade name Styrofoam. Nylon is also a polymer, as are epoxy materials like Superglue and polyurethane finishes for wood furniture and flooring. But people usually associate the word "plastic" with the first group of polymers. These are all thermoplastics, polymers that soften when they are heated and harden when cooled to room temperature.

The remaining part of the dictionary definition defines plastics as being able to be formed into objects and films using multiple methods. This attribute is crucial to the prominent role plastics play in modern society. Plastics are extremely versatile and compatible with high-volume, low-cost manufacturing.

▨ A brief history of plastics

Plastics are a relatively new class of materials, having existed for barely more than one hundred years. The first commercial synthetic plastic material dates to the early twentieth century. Leo Hendrik Baekeland created Bakelite, a thermosetting plastic formed by combining carbolic acid (also known as phenol) and formaldehyde. Baekeland founded the General Bakelite Company in 1910 to commercialize the product. It was marketed as a wonder material: hard, unbreakable, impervious to chemical attack, and fireproof.

Baekeland envisioned a world where nearly everything a person touched in daily life was made from Bakelite. While this has not come to pass, it is possible today to purchase a wide range of products made of Bakelite, from costume jewelry to cookware.

Many of the plastics in common use today were invented between 1930 and 1960. The 1930s saw neoprene, polystyrene, polyethylene, PVC, Plexiglas, polyurethanes, and nylon come to market. Polyethylene terephthalate (PET), polyimides, and polycarbonates followed in the next two decades. All these materials have valuable commercial uses. Reusable water bottles are made from PET. Polycarbonates are especially tough materials, used in eyeglasses and bulletproof windows. The "Development of Plastics" timeline gives the approximate dates when select plastics were first patented or manufactured.

Development of plastics
Approximate years when materials were first patented or manufactured

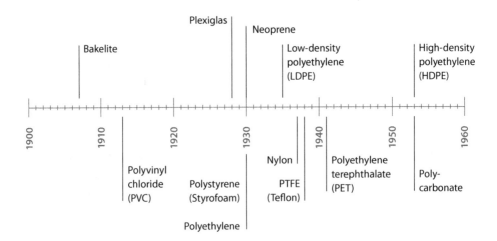

Conventional plastics start as hydrocarbon feedstocks derived from fossil fuels such as natural gas or crude oil. Polyethylene starts from ethylene, a hydrocarbon monomer (individual small molecule) that can be extracted from natural gas or by distilling crude oil. Similarly, propene is the basis for polypropylene. Combining ethylene and chlorine creates ethylene dichloride, which is converted into vinyl chloride to produce PVC.

It wasn't until around 1960 that the hydrocarbon feedstocks for plastics became readily available at low cost, greatly expanding commercial plastic production. Today more than 90 percent of plastics are made from virgin fossil-fuel feedstocks.

The fifty years between 1960 and 2010 saw a nearly forty-fold increase in annual global plastic production, which jumped from 8 million metric tons to more than 300 (see graph). Despite efforts to curb plastics usage in recent years, global plastics consumption continues to rise. Much of this increase is due to rising populations and expansion of the middle class in China.

▨ Hot polymers on a summer day

Polymers can be either thermoplastic or thermosetting. Thermoplastics make up the bulk of commercially produced polymers. As mentioned earlier, thermoplastic polymers soften when they are heated and harden when they

Increase in global plastic production,
millions of metric tons

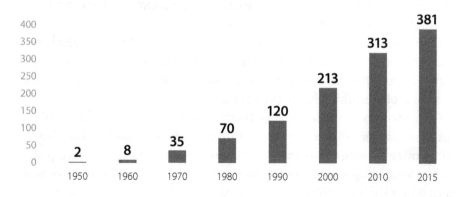

Data from Roland Geyer, Jenna R. Jambeck, and Kara Lavender Law,
"Production, Use, and Fate of All Plastics Ever Made"

are cooled. When heated to a sufficiently high temperature, thermoplastics flow like liquids and can be poured into molds. At room temperature, most thermoplastics are stable and long lasting, although some can soften if left in the sun on a hot day. It is possible to melt and reshape thermoplastics multiple times. This property makes them easier to recycle than thermosetting polymers. Used thermoplastics can be cleaned, ground into pieces, and then reheated to make new plastic products.

For me, talk of thermoplastics often brings to mind a specific image. It's 95 degrees outside, even hotter in the lab, and I'm standing over a huge vat of black goo, wearing only a tank top and shorts under my lab coat to avoid getting heatstroke. The summer after graduating from college I worked at Raychem in Menlo Park, California. My official title was "technician," since this was just a temporary job before grad school and I suppose the company wanted to preserve the engineering jobs for permanent hires. But a friendly applications engineer named Jeff knew I had an engineering degree and assigned me an engineering project.

My job was to test out different formulations of a specific thermoplastic material to determine which recipe would yield a material with the best match of properties for a particular application. I mixed translucent polymer beads with several additives in varying amounts and heated the whole mixture to melting, somewhere between 300 and 350 degrees Celsius (570 to 630 degrees Fahrenheit, hotter than a household oven).

The ingredient list included carbon black, a powdered form of carbon much like purified soot. The carbon black colored the polymer and made it slightly electrically conductive. A nugget for trivia buffs: a trio of scientists—Alan Heeger, Alan MacDiarmid, and Hideki Shirakawa—received the Nobel Prize in chemistry in 2000 for "the discovery and development of conductive polymers," based on research done in the 1970s.

Changing the amounts of the various additives affected the electrical conductivity and strength of the thermoplastic material I was making. In addition to a protective lab coat, goggles, and heat-resistant gloves, I also wore a mask to avoid breathing in the carbon black dust.

Once incorporated into the final thermoplastic material, the carbon black posed no danger. That is the case with many additives used in the chemical industry. So long as workplaces put appropriate safety measures in place, such as ventilating manufacturing labs and providing proper protective gear to employees, the additives are not hazardous to employees or customers.

Many producers of industrial chemicals like to advertise their materials as "safe when used as recommended" or some such language. But the manufacturers are not policing their customers' factories. Chemical suppliers hope that including appropriate usage directions, warnings, and safety recommendations will be sufficient to absolve them of legal responsibility should their industrial customers' employees become injured or ill after using their products.

Understanding common polymers

Most of the plastics in common use, including all those used for disposable plastic packaging, are thermoplastics. Polyethylene, polypropylene, and PVC are the most commercially important materials in this class. Chapter 7 revisits each of these thermoplastics, and other plastics used as disposable packaging, in more detail in the context of recycling.

Polyethylene

Polyethylene forms the basis for several common materials. In low-density polyethylene (LDPE) the molecules arrange themselves in a branched structure, with multiple small branches off of the primary chain. Like human hairs with split ends that branch off from the core, these molecules are not as strong as those where the hydrocarbon molecules arrange themselves in a single line. High-density polyethylene (HDPE) forms such a linear structure. The manufacturing process involves metallic chemicals called Ziegler-Natta catalysts, named after Karl Ziegler and Giulio Natta, who received the 1963 Nobel Prize in chemistry for their discovery. These catalysts allow the ethylene to polymerize at much lower pressures than those required to produce LDPE.

LDPE is a transparent material commonly made into films. HDPE is opaque and is both denser and stronger than LDPE. Linear LDPE, or LLDPE, is a material that may be considered to be an improved version of LDPE, combining the best features of both LDPE and HDPE. The structure is mostly linear, with occasional short branches, creating a material that is stronger than LDPE but still transparent to light. LLDPE can be stretched into very thin, relatively strong films.

Polypropylene

Polypropylene is known for having a high ratio of strength to density, making it useful for manufacturing both disposable containers and long-lasting storage bins. When woven into fibers, it's used to make strong ropes and indoor/outdoor carpet, the latter of which is usually made from recycled polypropylene.

Polypropylene has some disadvantages: it is flammable unless treated with potentially toxic flame retardants, and it degrades when exposed to sunlight.

Polyvinyl chloride

The hard plastic tubing used for water and sewage pipes is made from PVC. PVC has gotten bad press from organizations such as Greenpeace, who claim that its production, use, and disposal are contaminating the environment and harming consumers. Commercial PVC includes additives known as phthalates, plasticizers whose purpose is to soften the plastic for easier processing. It is possible for phthalates to leach out of water pipes made from PVC. They can also be released into the air if PVC is incinerated.

The US Centers for Disease Control and Prevention (CDC) conducted research showing the widespread prevalence of phthalates in human urine. At the same time, the CDC states that these results don't necessarily imply a public health problem and that "more research is needed to assess the human health effects of exposure to phthalates."

Meanwhile, manufacturers of PVC argue that the material is safe when used as intended and are concerned about the difficulty of replacing it with something that works as well. Such claims provide yet another example of the underlying challenge in removing toxins or suspected toxins, fueled by the desire of companies with a profitable product to continue promoting it. Public outcry against phthalates is, however, driving a trend toward PVC-free versions of consumer goods.

Thermosetting polymers

Thermosetting polymers achieve their properties through an irreversible chemical reaction. The most familiar example is epoxy glues. They come as a pair of liquids that, when mixed in the correct proportions, solidify within minutes at room temperature, forming a reliable, permanent bond to cement like or unlike materials to one another.

The time it takes a thermosetting polymer to solidify (cure) depends on both the temperature and the type of polymer. Epoxies cure fully within twenty-four hours. Polyurethane finishes, used to create a waterproof coating on wood, can take weeks to cure completely. During this time the liquid solvents in the polymer are slowly evaporating into the air, which is what causes the telltale odor. It is best to avoid breathing these solvent vapors, which is why epoxies and polyurethanes come with warnings to use only in areas with proper ventilation.

I do take these warnings seriously. I open the garage door when using epoxies to glue something together. When a leaking refrigerator damaged the wood floors in my kitchen, warping them beyond repair, I needed to get the floors replaced. I was well aware of the dangers of oil-based polyurethane finishes. The Swedish finish so popular in the Seattle area is especially toxic. Manufacturers suggest that it is best to keep babies and pets out of the home until the finish cures, which can take many weeks in the cool, damp Seattle climate.

The Swedish finish is durable and beautiful, which is why it has been popular. Of course, that is exactly the type of finish used when my floors were originally installed, long before I bought the house. After some searching, I found a contractor willing to finish my new floors with a water-based finish. My cat could safely enter the house as soon as the finish was dry (twenty-four hours after the final coat), and my family and I did not need to breathe toxic fumes. The resulting finish is not as shiny as Swedish, but it looks good enough to me.

Bioplastics: the wave of the future?

For some applications, people much prefer a product that looks, feels, and works like plastic. Paper isn't water resistant, and going back to metal or glass creates a heavier product that doesn't meet customer expectations and may require more energy to produce. Glass is susceptible to breaking, and metal is susceptible to rusting. How about instead creating a "better" plastic?

Bioplastics provide one route to addressing the carbon footprint and waste associated with conventional plastics. The term "bioplastic" can refer to one of two concepts:

- Biobased plastics, which are plastic materials made from recently living organisms (biomass) rather than fossil fuels
- Biodegradable plastics, which can degrade relatively quickly into simple elements and compounds

Rubber made from a rubber tree was the first true bioplastic, but when people talk about biobased plastics they usually aren't referring to natural rubber. Most existing biobased plastics are chemically the same as the conventional plastics they replace. For example, ethylene is the same compound whether derived from natural gas or ripening bananas, which emit ethylene gas. Polyethylene and PET are the most prevalent biobased plastics on the market, with 1.7 million metric tons produced in 2014. These materials are no more compostable than conventional polyethylene or PET.

Corn, wheat, and sugarcane are possible sources of biobased plastics. While these plastics eliminate the use of fossil fuels as sources of plastic feedstocks, the energy needed to manufacture plastics from agricultural sources likely comes from fossil fuels. These biobased plastics also require farmland and the associated water for irrigation. Land used to produce bioplastics exclusively is not available for food crops. The goal of agriculture is supposed to be to feed people, not to feed our ever-growing desire for more plastic stuff.

We can look at this problem in several ways. What about all the agricultural land that's being used to grow feed for cattle? If global beef consumption were to plummet as a result of advocacy for a more plant-based diet, then cattle farmers could convert their land to crops grown to produce biobased plastics or biofuels. They could, of course, choose to grow food crops instead, and would probably take whichever route was most likely to allow them to stay financially solvent.

Also, biomass does not need to be created from crops planted for that purpose. What about all the produce that farmers discard every year because it is blemished or otherwise can't be sold to consumers at a reasonable price? Sometimes it becomes animal feed. There is a growing movement to sell "ugly" produce at discounted prices rather than tossing it in a trash heap or compost bin. But scrap from food crops can be used as a source of biomass, alleviating the concern about dedicating acres of land to produce plastic.

Nonfood plants can also be a source of plastics created from biomass. Cellulose from trees could be processed into commercial plastics. It may even be possible to create plastics derived from algae. Such efforts are currently in the research phase.

Researchers are also developing another option: bioplastics sourced from captured greenhouse gas emissions. Methane can be recovered from landfills and coal mines. Industrial processes, such as metal or cement production, create carbon dioxide. Capturing the methane or carbon dioxide represents a new opportunity in the search for new sources of bioplastics. Several companies are working to bring such bioplastics out of the lab and into commercial production.

All biobased plastics sourced from greenhouse gases, and some of those sourced from biomass, are entirely new polymers, such as polylactic acid (PLA) or polyhydroxyalkanoate (PHA). PLA is gaining attention for its use in compostable serving ware designed to replace disposable clear plastic cups. As we will see later in this chapter, however, PLA is not necessarily as environmentally friendly as many people believe.

▓ Additives and contaminants

All commercial plastics contain a complex blend of chemical compounds, some of which are potentially hazardous to human health. In the case of thermosetting polymers, the inhalation danger passes once the product cures fully and all solvents have evaporated. Some plastics, however, contain additives that are toxic not only during manufacturing but potentially to those who use products made from the materials. Research suggests links between exposure to these toxic additives and increased rates of cancer, genetic mutations, and diabetes.

Additives in plastics give the materials valuable properties. They may increase the fire resistance of plastics, help them flow better during injection molding (a process that injects liquid plastic into a cool metal mold to create the desired shape), or infuse them with color that won't wash off. The manufacturers prioritized the desired end properties without worrying much about safety and toxicity. Wouldn't it be great to find replacements for many of these additives that allow producers to create less-toxic plastics? Those efforts are happening, but the solutions don't always solve the whole problem.

When thinking of toxic additives to plastic, bisphenol A (BPA) tops the list. BPA is found in polycarbonate plastics and gained notoriety because of baby bottles made from these materials. Babies and young children are more susceptible to toxins than older children and adults, so the presence of BPA in baby bottles was especially worrisome. Heating plastic food or beverage containers increases the likelihood of contaminants leaching out, and milk or formula is typically heated to body temperature before feeding to infants.

BPA is an endocrine disruptor. It mimics the hormone estrogen and is believed to affect brain and reproductive system development in those exposed to it early in life. A 2003 study showed that measurable levels of BPA in the urine of more than 90 percent of Americans. The Food and Drug Administration (FDA) banned the use of BPA in baby bottles in 2012, and the chemical now no longer appears in polycarbonates used in reusable bottles marketed to older children and adults.

The plastics industry responded to the demand for BPA-free plastics by substituting bisphenol S (BPS), a similar chemical that was believed to be less liable to leach into food or beverages stored in plastic containers. Unfortunately, it appears that BPS is risky as well and can cause the same type of health issues as BPA. Results from testing on animals, combined with data showing the presence of BPS in most Americans' urine, are frightening. Just because a container is BPA-free, it isn't necessarily safe.

What about just removing both BPA and BPS? That would create a safer polycarbonate, but such material could not be used for plastic bottles unless the industry can develop alternative plasticizers. Without a plasticizer, polycarbonate would be too brittle and susceptible to cracking during the molding process.

Some pigments used in labels contain lead or cadmium. These heavy metals are especially a problem in compostable plastics, since they contaminate the compost, potentially allowing the metals to enter the food chain when the compost is added to the soil. The presence of lead and cadmium also slows the process of bacterial growth in compost, which is essential to its function.

Certifications for compostable plastics specify strict limits on the acceptable level of heavy metals. The American Society for Testing Materials (ASTM) standard D6400-12 states that, for a plastic to be labeled compostable, it must contain less than half the EPA allowable concentration of toxic heavy metals. Is that sufficient to ensure safety and efficient breakdown of organic material in compost? I don't know. It would be best if manufacturers of compostable products could find 100 percent nontoxic inks for labeling.

Toxic additives hinder not only composting but also recycling. While these additives provide useful benefits when they are added to virgin materials during plastics manufacturing, they no longer improve material properties of the recycled plastics. Instead, they make these materials less pure and contribute to the perception that post-consumer waste is not safe. Removing the worst offending additives, if done while maintaining acceptable performance of plastics, improves the quality of recycled plastics and their economic value.

In an ideal world, it would be possible to replace all toxic additives with alternatives that are proved to be nontoxic while producing plastics that have equal or better performance and no increase in cost. But in the real world, alternatives that meet the toxicity criteria may not meet desired performance and cost goals. Unless public health is the top priority, rising above cost considerations, change will be slow.

In the US, the EPA maintains a list of Safer Chemical Ingredients. The government evaluates chemicals to screen for those known to cause cancer, genetic mutations, asthma, or damage to internal organs. To be given the green light, chemicals must not accumulate in the body under repeated exposure or cause endocrine disruption. Chemicals fall into one of several categories:

- Green circle: the chemical is verified to be of low concern
- Half green circle: the chemical appears to be of low concern, but future studies may be recommended

- Yellow triangle: the chemical may be best in its class of materials regarding toxicity and does meet minimum criteria, but still may be considered hazardous
- Grey square: the chemical does not meet criteria to be placed on the list

Having such a list should, in theory, keep the public safe from toxic chemicals, but that isn't necessarily the case. Not all companies go to the trouble of having their products tested and making sure they refrain from using ingredients that haven't passed the Safer Chemical screening. And the screening itself remains imperfect—new formulations and chemicals are being developed all the time, and the government doesn't have the time to evaluate all of them.

Teflon as an example

Growing awareness of product safety and public pressure are pushing more companies to reduce toxins in their products. The greater emphasis on safety helps companies that have long been promoting nontoxic products to have an increased presence in the global marketplace. This approach will only be successful, however, if the less toxic versions work as well as those they are replacing. Coatings on nonstick cookware serve as an example of the inherent challenge.

Polytetrafluoroethylene is better known by its acronym, PTFE. PTFE is the primary component of Teflon, trademarked by Chemours and originally developed by DuPont. The material has a very high melting point and low coefficient of friction, which means that coatings made from the material are extremely slippery. This property makes it desirable for coating nonstick cookware. Before 2015, nonstick cookware often also incorporated PFOA, the chemical that contaminated landfills and sickened cattle in West Virginia (see the story on page 34).

The desirable properties of PTFE coatings are also what makes the material difficult to manufacture. It doesn't melt and flow easily like other polymers. Manufacturing processes use very fine powders of PTFE, potentially exposing workers to dust. Proper workplace safety procedures can reduce, but not necessarily eliminate, such exposure.

Teflon coatings on cookware don't last forever, and as they slough off, they can be ingested with food. Concern about the toxicity of Teflon coatings, especially the toxic fumes that can be released if the coating is heated above a safe temperature, has led to a market for "greener" nonstick cookware.

Early attempts were not especially successful. In 2009, *Cook's Illustrated* magazine tested "green" skillets, those free of PFOA. The skillets were coated with either PTFE-based materials, polymers containing silicone, or ceramics. PTFE produced the best nonstick surface. Testers found the ceramic coatings to be severely lacking when it came to durability and nonstick performance. The article's conclusion? Customers wanting a chemical-free nonstick skillet should buy a cast iron pan, a product they call "the original green skillet." Yes, it's heavy, but it's safe, and it works.

A decade after *Cook's Illustrated* tested nonstick skillets, the latest trend in nonstick cookware is pots and pans coated with a copper-infused ceramic that gives the cookware a distinctive reddish-brown copper appearance. The core is aluminum, just like in previous generations of nonstick and regular cookware. These pans are free from PFOA and PTFE, but reviews suggest that the nonstick performance isn't as long-lasting as promised. Perhaps *Cook's Illustrated* is still right about cast iron. Meanwhile, concerns about plastic reach beyond PTFE coatings.

The plastic trash problem

Aside from concerns about toxins, the biggest problem with plastics is what happens to them after people discard them. Plastic packaging is the largest source of plastic trash, because these are products designed to have a very short useful life, less than a year from when they are manufactured and some-times less than an hour from when they arrive in a consumer's hands. Though their useful life is short, disposable plastics can last on this planet for over a century.

The plastic grocery bag stands as the prototypical example of plastic trash. Americans use 100 billion plastic bags each year (that's more than 250 million per day), and our country is not even close to the worst offender worldwide when it comes to sources of plastic trash.

Mentioning plastic bags, especially when associated with the word "ban," is a surefire way to start a spirited discussion. Some environmental groups have made enacting plastic bag bans a key element of their platform. They are certainly tackling other issues, but plastic bags get people's attention.

Public opinion on plastic bags primarily falls into two camps: those who believe bags are a danger to the environment and should be banned, and those who think the government has no place regulating what types of bags their local grocery store should be allowed to carry. In an online discussion in my neighborhood in 2017, those opposing the idea of a potential citywide ban outnumbered those in favor by a margin of more than four to one.

Those against banning plastics bags often point out their usefulness. They are effective for carrying groceries, with convenient handles that make it easy to carry several bags in one hand. They handle wet groceries without breaking or disintegrating. Once the bags are home from the grocery store, they come in handy for lining trash cans or disposing of used cat litter. Why buy new bags for that purpose rather than reusing those from the store?

Even though some tout the benefits of plastic bags, the tide is turning against single-use plastics. Earth Day 2018 centered programming around the theme of plastic trash. More and more cities are banning various types of disposable plastics, from grocery bags to drinking straws.

Despite the efforts of those who reuse plastic bags and dispose of them properly, far too many plastic bags—and other types of plastic trash—are ending up in the oceans. It is the presence of plastic trash in rivers, lakes, and oceans that is causing the greatest concern.

Most of the plastic in the oceans comes from packaging. According to the Ellen MacArthur Foundation, at least eight million tons of plastic enters the oceans each year, the equivalent of a garbage truck full of plastic trash every minute. The economic impact of ocean plastic is astounding. Globally, the presence of plastics in the oceans costs tourism, fishing, and shipping industries $13 billion per year.

The statistics are alarming, but for citizens in North America and Europe, it may seem far removed from our own lives. It is easy to get complacent if we don't personally see the damage. From our viewpoint, the trash seems to be under control. In many cities, curbside collection is inexpensive and reliable.

Countries in Asia are responsible for the vast majority of plastic trash in the oceans. A 2017 study concluded that between 88 and 95 percent of plastics in the oceans flow there from ten large rivers. These include the Yangtze, Indus, and six other rivers in Asia, plus the Nile and Niger rivers in Africa. The presence of large populations near riverbanks, combined with a lack of waste collection and containment systems, has created this problem over several decades.

An island of plastic

The Great Pacific Garbage Patch is somewhat of a misnomer. Despite the image the name may suggest, no large plastic island in the Pacific Ocean can be seen from space, or even from an airplane. The Pacific Garbage Patch is, however, real. Most of the trash lies beneath the surface, and much of it consists of microplastic.

Plastic fragments less than around 5 mm in size—there is no agreed-upon exact cutoff—are termed microplastic, while larger pieces are called macroplastic. Macroplastic debris is an eyesore and can pose a suffocation or strangling hazard to marine animals.

While plastic debris exists throughout the world's oceans, currents concentrate it in specific regions, such as the two large collections of debris in the North Pacific Gyre. Coastal areas also exhibit a much higher concentration of plastic debris than the open ocean.

Henderson Island, an uninhabited, remote island in the South Pacific, stands as a prime example of the prevalence of macroplastic. The island made international news headlines in 2017 when Australian researchers published results of a study showing that Henderson's beaches are covered in more than thirty-seven million pieces of trash, much of it being discarded plastic items. Henderson is only fourteen square miles. Currents have been washing trash ashore from locations as far-flung as China, Japan, and Chile.

Trash-strewn beaches around the world provide a visible reminder of the problems that plastic trash is causing and make for compelling photographs. But microplastic is a problem that is just as worrisome, if not more so.

When plastic packaging starts to degrade as a result of exposure to sun and oxygen, it breaks down into small fragments. This process is part of the reason that concentrations of microplastics in the oceans have increased significantly since the 1960s. The plastic trash that has been accumulating for decades continues to break down into smaller pieces. At some point, these microplastic bits do not further degrade but are small enough for fish and other marine animals to eat. This type of debris is called secondary microplastic.

Primary microplastics are posing a growing concern. These are from sources that are manufactured as small plastic particles. One example is so-called microbeads or microexfoliates, synthetic alternatives to ground almonds or pumice in facial cleansers. Plastic microbeads are made from polyethylene, polypropylene, or polystyrene. These plastic particles, which range from under 0.1 mm to around 5 mm in size and enter waterways when washed down drains, are a growing source of microplastics in the oceans.

Heavy industry creates another source of microplastics in the ocean. Acrylic, melamine, or polyester particles are sometimes used in air blasters to clean paint or rust off of machinery, engines, or boat hulls. The paint residue may contain heavy metals, especially if it dates from the 1960s or earlier, causing not only microplastics but toxic metals to contaminate waterways.

The concentration of microplastics in the oceans increased significantly in the second half of the twentieth century, but accurately measuring it presents a challenge. The oceans are incredibly vast, and distribution of microplastics is not uniform. Concentrations in local regions increase after storms or hurricanes, for example.

Concentrations can be measured directly by taking samples of ocean water or sediment from the sea floor. Results depend on the size of the mesh used to trap microplastics. In one study, an 80-micron mesh resulted in a concentration 100,000 times that obtained with a 450-micron mesh in the same region at the same time.

Another common approach to measuring microplastic concentrations gives some alarming results. Examination of the gut contents of fish or seabirds shows an incredibly high percentage of creatures with ingested plastic. Plastic fragments were first observed in seabirds back in the 1960s, and a 2011 study of fulmars, an ocean-foraging bird species, showed an average of twenty-six plastic fragments in the gut of each bird. The fact that this value has remained stable since 2000 is slightly encouraging. At least it isn't still increasing.

Research has still not confirmed whether microplastics ingested by marine animals move up the food chain when other animals, including humans, eat the seafood. At present, it appears that the presence of mercury in fish is more of a danger than plastics, at least from the viewpoint of those eating the fish.

Goal: reduce plastics usage

Project Mainstream, an initiative developed by the World Economic Forum and the Ellen MacArthur Foundation, published a report in 2016 called *The New Plastics Economy*. This report lays out the organizations' vision—a world in which plastics are never sent to landfills nor end up in the oceans but are continually recycled until the point where they have outlived their usefulness and can biodegrade. This vision will be easier to achieve if fewer plastics enter the world in the first place.

Several approaches can be considered to reduce the amount of plastics being produced. These include:

- Reducing the weight of existing plastic products by changing the design. Plastic water bottles demonstrate an example of this approach. Over the years, the layer of plastic has become thinner and caps have become smaller. (I would argue that getting rid of disposable plastic water bottles entirely would be a better solution.)

- Replacing plastics with materials that were in common use before plastics became so pervasive. For example, glass storage containers are becoming more popular, although they do sometimes come with plastic lids.

- Improving recycling rates so that more products are made from recycled plastic rather than from virgin material. Such efforts should ideally be combined with improving recycling technology.
- Replacing conventional plastics with polymers produced without fossil fuels. This action doesn't reduce the total amount of plastic being produced but may reduce the carbon footprint associated with plastic production.

All these approaches have their benefits and drawbacks, not all of which are obvious at first glance.

Design changes aimed at reducing the weight of a product may cause problems with performance. Thinner water bottles are much flimsier than the previous generation of bottles they replaced. For durable goods, reducing weight may make them less durable, causing them to be replaced more frequently and negating any benefits. Small plastic parts that break and render a product useless are not just annoying, but wasteful. 3-D printing, discussed in more detail in Part III, presents a possible solution. Simply print a replacement part, and the product is as good as new.

Switching out plastics for other materials may come with unintended consequences. Replacing the plastic grocery bag with a paper or reusable bag, for example, would seem to be an environmentally sound decision, but that is not necessarily the case. Plastic grocery bags were first introduced in the US in 1979 and became popular more than a decade later, helped by a marketing strategy that promoted them as being less expensive and stronger than paper bags. Unlike plastic, paper bags can disintegrate when exposed to water.

The environmental benefit of replacing plastic bags is not obvious when considering the energy and water used to produce various types of bags. Paper bags are usually made from virgin sources rather than recycled paper because recycled paper is not as strong. Production of paper requires resources: trees and water, plus the energy needed to process the wood into pulp and then process the pulp into paper. Producing a paper bag requires four times as much water as producing a plastic bag.

This calculation, however, does not take into account the fact that the same groceries when bagged in paper typically use less than half the number of bags they would if bagged in plastic. Unless, of course, baggers double-bag the paper because they don't think it's strong enough to carry heavy groceries.

Improving rates of plastic recycling is a good strategy—one that we will cover in greater detail in Chapter 6—but there are limits to the effectiveness of recycling. Replacing conventional plastics with those not made from fossil fuels makes a lot of sense. This approach doesn't solve all the problems inherent in using plastics, but it is worth considering.

Biodegradable plastics are not all the same. Some biodegrade much more rapidly than others. In order to be industrially compostable, materials have to meet several criteria. They must:

- Degrade at least 90 percent by weight within six months at an industrial composting facility
- Contain at least 50 percent organic matter
- Contain no more than a specified concentration of heavy metals
- Disintegrate into fragments smaller than 2 mm within twelve weeks under controlled composting conditions
- Create compost that is nontoxic, meaning that it will create no negative health effects when used as a soil amendment for food crops

The performance and price of compostable materials have improved significantly in recent years. Compostable bags, plates, and utensils are sufficiently strong to withstand use, allowing them to fulfill their purpose and help return nutrients from food waste back to the soil.

Industrially compostable bioplastics generally require a combination of water and heat to decompose properly. PLA, the material most commonly found in compostable plastic cups, falls into this category. The requirement of adding water and heat is an important concept, since PLA may not decompose if discarded into the trash, nor will it degrade in rivers or oceans. Cups made from PLA will best serve their intended purpose if discarded with food waste into bins headed for commercial composting facilities. They should not be placed into recycling bins, where they will contaminate the recycling stream if not segregated.

The availability of curbside composting for residents in some communities has created a market for compostable bags for collecting food waste. These bags are "certified compostable" and can be deposited into containers intended for compost. A box of such bags from BioBag Americas claims to use resins sourced from Italy, made with "starches from renewable crops free from GMOs."

In my community, food waste bagged in compostable bags joins yard waste in a single, large bin. Increasing adoption of composting is an especially effective way to reduce the volume of waste being sent to landfills since uneaten food makes up the largest single component of municipal solid waste. Of course, larger-scale adoption relies on the availability of local industrial composting facilities.

Compostable products extend well beyond bags for collecting food waste. An entire new industry is developing with compostable products meant to replace plastic flatware, Styrofoam takeout containers, and more. My interview with Mark Stephany of World Centric, a company that produces containers made from a variety of plant-based materials, appears below.

INTERVIEW   Mark Stephany, World Centric

Mark's interest in social and environmental responsibility developed relatively late in life, after a thirty-year career in sales in the food manufacturing industry. Mark worked for such giants as Kraft, Nabisco, and Kellogg, and still believes that these are worthwhile companies with initiatives related to positive change in the world. But, he said, he needed a nudge to become aware of the opportunity to truly consider the impact of his work. Mark's journey started with a conversation with a recruiter who specializes in Benefit Corporations (more on those in Chapter 9). Mark was inspired and decided to switch gears to work for a company where doing the right thing holds a higher priority than maximizing profits.

After two years as head of sales at World Centric, Mark feels that he made the right move. He is proud of the company where he works, one that donates 25 percent of its profits to improving the lives of people in impoverished regions of the world. The company has built a school in Haiti and provided mosquito netting to people living in malaria-inflicted areas, fresh drinking water to communities in sub-Saharan Africa, and toilets to villages in India.

Mark talked to me about World Centric's products and supply chain. Its flatware and cold-drink cups are made from corn-based PLA, which it receives in pellet form from its supplier, Nature Works. Some of World Centric's products make use of agricultural waste or biowaste. Wheat straw—the residual plant stalks not used in food production—are usually discarded. Farmers either leave the straw in the fields to rot or burn it. World Centric repurposes this wheat straw to create molded fiber-based clamshell containers, plates, and bowls that replace similar products made from Styrofoam. Leftover plant stalks from sugar cane (bagasse) can be used in the same manner. The dry, pulpy, fibrous residue that remains after sugarcane or sorghum stalks are crushed to extract their juice is usually burned.

All of World Centric's packaging products are fully compostable in industrial composting facilities, meaning that they turn back into soil within three to six months. If these plant-based packages are discarded in a landfill, however, they will not decompose any faster than most of the other materials languishing there, as it is an anaerobic environment, lacking the oxygen present in industrial composting facilities. Still, even in the case where consumers discard the biobased packaging into a landfill, the material can require less energy to produce than traditional plastics, depending on production methods. Also, many consumers are shifting to compostable fiber containers to reduce the risk of toxins leaching from petroleum-based containers when microwaving leftovers.

While educated consumers have been focusing on where their food comes from for some time, packaging hasn't gotten the same level of attention until more recently. Mark hopes to accelerate the next stage in consumer education, centered around packaging. Certain regions in the US, especially along the West Coast, are familiar with the idea of reducing conventional plastic packaging, but the message is quickly spreading to other parts of the country.

Mark is succeeding in getting more restaurants to use plant-based packaging. Even if the restaurants can't control what the consumer does with a takeout container when it leaves the premises, offering compostable packaging is a start. Restaurants want their customers to see they are doing the right thing.

Epic Burger, a restaurant chain in Chicago, is one of World Centric's customers. They proudly display their Epic Rules, one of which is "Packaging Made from Plants." Mark has noticed greater interest in plant-based packaging from public school districts, driven by parent pressure to avoid Styrofoam. Some of these schools are creating on-site compost piles to collect food waste and plant-based packaging. The programs are educational and redirect waste destined for the landfill.

The backend composting infrastructure for food and packaging waste does exist, but it's still developing. Composting is still new in many parts of the country and policies vary—for example, the state of Oregon approaches composting very differently than do California and Washington (see page 206). Mark sees composting as a great potential moneymaking venture, both for collecting the compostable material and for selling the processed compost. Greater concern about the amount of trash generated and limits to landfill space will drive more composting.

Mark understands the resistance to switching to plant-based packaging. As he points out, Styrofoam is inexpensive and readily available. Other options will cost more. Mark's advice for companies wanting to make a switch toward more environmentally friendly packaging options is to budget in the cost difference as an up-front cost. As an example, a children's hospital calculated that the cost of switching from Styrofoam to plant-based packaging was $250,000 per year. The hospital administration looked at the message they wanted to send as a company in the health care industry and considered the additional cost as an investment in their brand.

Mark is optimistic about the future of plant-based packaging. As demand grows, costs will eventually need to come down. Meanwhile, World Centric tries to keep costs as low as reasonable to help bridge the gap while they wait for the packaging industry to catch up. Mark believes in building awareness, dispelling greenwashing, and doing his part to educate people.

Toward better compostables

Not all compostable flatware is of the same level of quality. I recall a lunch event where all the forks (compostable products from a company other than World Centric) were falling apart as we tried to cut our chicken. Tines were breaking off, and handles were breaking in two. It was both amusing and frustrating. The chicken wasn't especially tough, but the forks just weren't up to the job. It's great to have flatware that composts, but not if it falls apart when we're using it. Products that create less waste to landfill are wonderful in theory. But if they don't perform, no one is going to buy them.

Part of the issue is that using more material—making fork tines thicker—makes a product more expensive. In a niche where products are already more expensive than the conventional plastics they are replacing, this can put the supplier in a difficult position. The more material used, the longer a product will take to compost as well. The trick is finding the right balance. Plant-based PLA can produce strong flatware that is no thicker than conventional plastic products and serves its purpose well, but it needs to be properly designed.

In addition to concerns about the performance of compostable plastics, their environmental benefits are not clear cut. The Oregon Department of Environmental Quality (DEQ) compared the life cycles of compostable and non-compostable food-service products by reviewing scientific literature and came to some counterintuitive conclusions. A DEQ report cited a study showing that composting compostable food packaging (primarily PLA) created a greater negative environmental and health impact than either using non-compostable packaging or recycling compostable packaging. The issues stem from the resources needed to make compostable products and the cross-contamination that occurs when people accidentally put non-compostable packaging into a compost bin (see the section about compliance on page 127).

Not all compostable products degrade as quickly as assumed. Even for those that do, compostable service ware does not improve the quality of compost because, unlike food waste, most degrade to carbon dioxide rather than useful biomass. The presence of food waste, however, helps food-service ware degrade in industrial composting facilities. At large public events, providing compostable serving ware and replacing trash cans with compost bins reduces food waste because people aren't tossing leftover food into bins destined for the landfill. The environmental benefit of less food waste probably overrides the impact of producing the compostable plates, cups, and forks.

Environmentally friendly new materials

Materials science promises the excitement of new materials that have never before existed, designed specifically to solve a particular problem. From a human health or environmental impact viewpoint, however, new materials are not necessarily better than those they aim to replace. This section focuses on new materials that have been created with sustainability and safety in mind, highlighting a few examples.

I have already mentioned bioplastics that are designed to look and feel much like the fossil-fuel-based materials they replace. In some cases, the resulting materials are chemically identical to conventionally produced plastics. In other cases, companies are inventing substitutes for common plastics that serve the function of the materials they are replacing but don't directly mimic them. These new materials creatively incorporate additional desirable features. Some have the potential to be revolutionary, creating new markets or changing the ways products are packaged or shipped.

Replacing Styrofoam packaging

Plant fibers make an effective substitute for Styrofoam clamshell food packaging and might eventually completely replace it. The reason they haven't already is an all-too-common problem: cost. Styrofoam is very inexpensive, and alternatives haven't reached the volume production necessary for costs to come down. With pressure from consumers and regulations at the city level, however, there may soon be enough businesses willing to buy plant-based clamshell packages and other containers at a premium. When that happens, the packaging industry should be able to bring costs down and mass production may become a reality.

Styrofoam is used in many more applications than just clamshell packaging. It's used to protect items being shipped. When replacing Styrofoam packing "peanuts" or solid forms shaped to protect furniture or electronics, stiff plant-based fiberboard will not do the job. Product shipping requires a different type of plant-based product to replace Styrofoam.

Compostable versions of Styrofoam "peanuts" have existed for years, in the form of cornstarch-based pellets. These aren't as sturdy as Styrofoam, but they serve their limited purpose. They can protect items that aren't especially fragile, and when they are no longer needed they quickly dissolve in water.

Cornstarch-based pellets aren't strong enough to replace Styrofoam in custom-molded shapes designed to protect delicate products during shipping. This application needs a more out-of-the-box alternative. One such option now exists.

Ecovative, based in Green Island, New York, makes a mushroom-based product that takes compostable packing material a step further. The material is grown from waste feedstock, in a new twist on additive manufacturing. Products are made from mycelium (mushroom roots) and agricultural fibers and take about a week to grow. Ecovative is gaining traction, having been awarded a contract from Dell to protect its computers for shipping. Still, its slow manufacturing process is likely to limit mass adoption at a global scale.

Less wasteful cleaning products

Polyvinyl alcohol (PVOH) possesses the useful property of being soluble in water while resisting damage from oils and oil-based solvents. Once dissolved in water, PVOH films are biodegradable.

Monosol manufactures water-soluble films made from PVOH that wrap single-use dishwasher and laundry detergent pods. Such products are now in common use. They are especially compelling because they enable an individually packaged consumer good to create less waste than the same product packaged in a large bottle. They fulfill the goal of convenience and ease of use, important criteria for consumer acceptance of a new concept.

Detergent pods have drawn negative attention because the products are so colorful that young children have mistaken the pods for candy. Although PVOH is safe, the detergent inside is not, especially since it's in a very concentrated form. The manufacturers could choose to remove the bright colors, which provides the added benefit of removing the coloring agents in laundry detergents that cause rashes in people with sensitive skin. Some manufacturers are moving in this direction while also reducing packaging waste. Tide has created a version of its laundry detergent pods that comes in a roll of tear-away pods without any additional packaging. The packaging is printed in color with water-soluble ink, but the detergent inside is clear.

Plastics that capture carbon

Making plastics from fossil-fuel sources creates carbon emissions. The strategies listed in this chapter aim to reduce the impact, but what if plastics could capture carbon emissions? It sounds a bit farfetched, but research at Columbia University demonstrated that sheets of polypropylene embedded with particles of a resin designed for purifying water could absorb carbon dioxide. In twenty-four hours, a small sheet of the material can absorb a quantity of CO_2 equal to the amount of the gas that thirteen people breathe out in a day.

Columbia professor Klaus Lackner once envisioned forests of this wonder material. According to his calculations, ten million artificial "trees" made with it could absorb enough CO_2 to reduce levels by 0.5 ppm per year. (1 ppm, which stands for *parts per million,* is 0.0001 percent.) Just like real trees, these artificial trees would need to be watered regularly. The material dries out as it absorbs CO_2, so too little water and it will cease to work. It also works best in a dry climate. If the air is too humid, then the material absorbs too much water and overheats.

An attempt to make a commercial version of Lackner's idea failed, as the market wasn't ready. It still may not be ready, and perhaps it never will be. Where do you "plant" millions of artificial trees? Los Angeles is a possibility. The LA basin is technically a desert, and with Hollywood and Disneyland nearby, fake trees should fit right in. Joking aside, the idea of using plastic to reduce, rather than add to, pollution has something compelling about it.

INTERVIEW   Sam Hopkins, EcoSheep

Inspiration can come from strange places. Sam Hopkins, the founder of EcoSheep and an avid cyclist, took his from a woolly animal. Some years ago, Sam's new bicycle developed an annoying squeak. He bought several commercial lubricants and started testing them out, spraying them on the bike chain. He noticed a warning label on one of the containers saying, "Danger: long-lasting effects to aquatic life." Living in an area where any storm runoff drains into a local pond, he became worried about the conventional bicycle chain lubricants and decided to create a better option.

Sam happened to have a gallon of sheep oil in his garage. I have many items in my garage, but I expect that I'm in the majority when I say that sheep oil is not one of them. But being unconventional seems to come naturally to Sam, and he was an aspiring entrepreneur interested in chemistry and the cosmetics industry, so storing a gallon of sheep oil made sense.

Lanolin, the oil found in sheep wool, has found commercial use for decades, primarily in cosmetics like lipstick and lotions. Just as human hair gets oily when it isn't washed, from the oils in our skin, wool gets oily. Before spinning sheep wool into yarn, this oil needs to be removed. An entire industry exists to extract the lanolin from wool and package it in large barrels.

It shouldn't be surprising that lanolin makes a great lubricant. Sam explained that long before petroleum lubricants existed, farmers used to run their metal tools through sheep wool to clean and protect the tools.

Sam and a friend were planning on using the sheep oil in Sam's garage to create an eco-friendly product to clean guitar strings. Existing eco-friendly oils were too slippery to use on guitar strings. Lanolin, on the other hand, has a slight tackiness to it. Rubbing sheep wool on the strings is an effective way to clean them. The abrasiveness of the wool, combined with the slightly tacky lanolin within it, make a good combination.

Unlike motor oil, which comes in different grades designed in a lab to work well in different weather conditions, lanolin is a natural oil designed to protect the sheep year-round. It naturally consists of multiple molecules that are made to keep the sheep's wool lubricated in all types of weather. The all-weather nature of lanolin makes it a versatile substance.

The bike chain lubrication problem, however, called out to Sam. At first glance, his estimate that bike riders in the US consume 6.3 million gallons of petroleum-based lubricants every year sounds a bit high. Sam based his estimate on 186 million bicycles in the US (a believable number), each using several ounces of lubricant. But many of those bicycles are sitting in garages, not being ridden, and even many people who do ride their bikes don't regularly maintain them. I know I was guilty of not lubricating my bicycle chain regularly, and I participate in triathlons!

Sam explained to me that both professionals at bicycle shops and individuals at home often use a great deal more lubricant on a bike than might be necessary, because they spray it onto the bike chain. Conventional lubricants come in spray cans. The lubricant gets everywhere, not just on the parts that need to be oiled. Lubricant is also used to clean gummed-up chains by soaking them in pails of the stuff. This additional information makes Sam's estimate of 6.3 million gallons sound more reasonable.

Sam buys barrels of lanolin to produce his line of EcoSheep lubricants. The product comes in a small metal can with a brush applicator that looks a rubber cement bottle—because that's exactly what it is. Sam was able to use an existing packaging product, helping keep costs under control by avoiding the need to design custom packaging, and the metal cans are recyclable.

The brush is a convenient way to apply just as much oil as needed rather than spraying oil everywhere. The user simply paints lubricant directly onto the chain, with no waste. The product is a bit unusual in the green product industry, in that it works better than the product it is replacing. Reviews on Amazon bear this out—everyone indeed seems to love it. I tried it, and I agree. I now lubricate my bike chain much more often.

Walmart's decision to partner with the EPA Safer Choice program and replace toxic products on its shelves with nontoxic ones provided Sam the perfect entry into high-volume sales. His path of entry was through Walmart's Made in America initiative supporting small businesses in this country. Walmart has committed to buying billions of dollars' worth of US-built products. EcoSheep still had to jump through hoops and demonstrate the environmental benefits of its products to get them into Walmart stores, but as of late 2017, Sam's products were in 900 Walmart stores.

EcoSheep is a member of Green America, a coalition of environmentally friendly companies. Green America works with its members to help them think about issues such as waste. EcoSheep has been inspired to make some purposeful decisions, such as buying steel drums rather than plastic ones to mix their products before packing into the rubber cement containers.

Sam believes in keeping manufacturing local, making the lubricant out of a warehouse in Pennsylvania. The Made in America concept even extends to the metal cans used to package the EcoSheep products for consumers—the cans are made in Connecticut, and the lids are made in Pennsylvania.

When production ramped up enough that Sam needed help getting products out the door, he partnered with a company in Ohio that was in the business of filling containers with petroleum products. He ships drums of lubricant to Ohio and the company uses its existing equipment to dispense the lubricant into individual cans and apply labels. The workers in Ohio can use their skills to package an eco-friendly product, and EcoSheep can ship more sheep oil.Lanolin has many potential uses, some of which may come as a surprise. Sam learned that every time a train goes around a bend in the track, an employee on board the train sprays petroleum oil directly onto the tracks. Doing so saves on gas because it reduces friction. Railroad companies found that it costs less to pay the EPA a fine from spraying the petroleum than to pay for the extra gas they would need to buy if they didn't apply the petroleum. Sam is working to develop a sprayable version of EcoSheep designed for the railroad industry.

I asked Sam about the potential to expand lanolin applications even further. Today no one is making plastics from lanolin feedstocks, but it isn't out of the question. It is certainly possible to imagine a lanolin-based plastic, although Sam pointed out that fitting it into trends toward plant-based products poses a certain marketing challenge. Vegans might have an issue with using animal oil.

CHAPTER 5

Light and Heavy Metals

"At first you need to do the right things, and
then you need to do those things right."

—Joe Fjelstad, Verdant Electronics

Where do metals come from?

Metals come from the Earth, but extracting the minerals in which they reside is a messy, expensive, dangerous, and destructive process. Improvements in mineral extraction and processing methods, as well as more efficient transportation and distribution, can go a long way toward reducing the amount of energy needed to create metals. But there is a limit to how effective such changes can be. Metal production remains energy-intensive.

I ought to know something about mining. After all, I defended my PhD dissertation in the Hearst Memorial Mining Building at UC Berkeley. That building was the headquarters for the Materials Science and Engineering Department. It is a beautiful historic building, completed in 1907, that was retrofitted in 2002 to meet earthquake-related building codes. Given that a UC Berkeley press release lists the location of the building as "800 feet west of the Hayward fault," the retrofit was a wise move.

In 1907, 20 percent of male students at UC Berkeley majored in mining (presumably there weren't any female students in the department). Those students crushed rocks and created metals in that very building. By the time I was in college, though, mining engineers were a bit of an anachronism. Civil engineers and geologists are now the ones involved in mining, attempting to make it safer and more efficient.

The early twentieth century may have been the heyday of mining, but its origins are much, much older. The invention of smelting—the process of heating mineral ores to extract the metals inside—is what brought civilization from the Stone Age to the Bronze Age. Ancient people discovered that when they crushed ores and heated them, the oxygen burned off and metal remained. Multiple cycles of heating produced ever-purer metals as contaminants with lower melting points burned off.

Copper, smelted from copper sulfide ores, was the first metal to be widely mined. Combining soft copper with tin created bronze, the first alloy. Hence, the aptly titled Bronze Age.

Iron and steel

The discovery of magnetite, an ore rich in iron, brought about the Iron Age. Iron smelted in charcoal furnaces ended up with a small percentage of carbon incorporated between the iron atoms, creating the first steel. Forging—beating on the steel while it was hot—distributed the carbon atoms more uniformly.

During the 1700s, steel became increasingly popular for forging nails, horseshoes, swords, and tools. Over the next century, improvements in smelting made steel production a much less energy-intensive process.

Today, basic oxygen furnaces, using a combination of iron and scrap steel, are used to produce much of the steel in the world. In the US, electric arc furnaces are more common. These furnaces use solely scrap metal. As of 2000, 60 percent of US steel was produced using arc furnaces, but only 10 percent of steel production in China took advantage of this type of equipment.

Processing methods can be chosen with energy savings in mind. Continuous casting of hot metal, as opposed to casting individual ingots and then reheating them to roll into the final desired shape, creates less scrap metal and saves up to 75 percent of the energy needed for casting and forming.

Varying the type and quantity of alloying elements—carbon plus various metals added to the steel—produces steel with a specific composition and with properties tailored to the end use. Stainless steel, for example, contains up to 20 percent chromium, which makes it resistant to corrosion. Other alloying elements improve the strength of the steel or make it easier to form into thin sheets.

PLANT TOUR Nucor Steel

I enjoyed the opportunity to tour Nucor Steel in Seattle and see firsthand how they turn scrap steel into the reinforcing bars (rebar) that strengthen concrete. We were a small group: the environmental engineer leading the tour, a newly hired engineer who wanted to gain insight into the production process, and the three women besides myself who had signed up for the tour. After grabbing disposable earplugs and donning hard hats, goggles, and bright orange jackets, we were ready to walk through the facility.

The Seattle facility is a mini mill, a designation that refers not to the size of the facility nor its production volume but to the energy efficiency of its steel producing operations. Nucor opened its first mini mill in 1969 to provide steel for its division that produced steel joists for the construction industry. The company has since expanded production and as of 2018 operates sixty-six plants in twenty-five US states making dozens of different steel products.

Nucor's micro mills, built in 2002 or later, provide the ultimate in energy efficiency. At those plants, molten steel gets turned into thin steel sheets in a single step. No energy is wasted by cooling the steel and then reheating it to shape it into its final form. In Seattle, the steel goes through a less efficient but equally fascinating process.

Steel production starts with scrap steel that arrives in Seattle by truck, rail, or barge from the western US and Canada. Each plant minimizes the need to add alloying elements to the steel by taking in scrap from sources that provide steel with a composition as close as possible to that of the final product. Some of the scrap shipped to Seattle comes from car junkyards, where old cars get dismantled and the chassis shredded into piles of debris.

During the tour, we walked by the mountains of scrap and got to see electromagnets several feet in diameter pick up loads of shredded steel and dump it into a charge bucket. Once the charge buckets are fully loaded with 100,000 pounds of steel, they move on overhead tracks into a warehouse-like building that houses the electric arc furnace. The furnace holds three buckets' worth of steel.

We walked upstairs to a glass-enclosed room where an employee sat in front of an array of computer monitors. He pointed out the screens displaying views from the multiple cameras located throughout the building and a chart showing the temperature of the steel inside the furnace. The man seemed glad to have company and a short break from his work. I imagine the job must be monotonous until one of the displays shows a problem and he needs to spring into action.

A charge bucket slid into view and its clamshell bottom opened up, dumping the contents into a huge container called a ladle. As the electric arc furnace cranked up, the graphite electrodes that melted the steel scrap glowed a blinding white. The heat was intense enough to feel, even from behind insulated glass walls. The temperature gauge climbed to 3,100 degrees Fahrenheit. Our tour guide explained that the temperature probes are dual-function, monitoring the temperature of the molten steel and extracting samples for chemical analysis. The on-site lab measures the chemical composition to ensure consistency.

The ladle containing the molten steel is itself made from steel, lined with brick to keep the ladle from melting. The ladle moves into a different part of the building to cast the steel into long beams called billets. Molten steel pours out of the bottom of the ladle from four openings into hollow copper molds with a six-inch-square cross section. The molds are lined with chrome on the inside and water-cooled from the outside to maintain exactly the right temperature and ensure that the copper doesn't melt. After following a curved path, the resulting steel billets need to be straightened. This step occurs when the steel is in the soft-boiled-egg stage—solid on the outside and still liquid in the middle.

If the outer casing isn't properly cooled, molten steel can break through. That sounds scary, but safety procedures ensure that workers maintain a sufficient distance. By the time the steel bars emerge from the molds and make their way onto outdoor cooling racks, they are completely solid. They are still hot, around 1,100 degrees. The presence of dozens of hot bars of steel warms the surrounding air considerably. The warmth wasn't unwelcomed on the cool fall day when I visited, but I'm sure it would feel sweltering in the heat of summer.

The steel bars make their way to the rolling room with the help of a conveyor belt, propelled by cables that look like thick, dirty bicycle chains. Debris accumulates on the chains and eventually sheds off onto the ground below. At this steel mill where recycling is embedded in production, even the debris is valuable. It gets swept up and sold to concrete manufacturers, who mix it into their concrete to achieve the optimal iron content.

Steel manufacturing uses a lot of water, and this too is recycled. The water that flows along copper casings to cool the steel billets is reused as many times as possible. As the water evaporates, the steam passes through filters and exits out the top of the building. Chimneys that look like smokestacks aren't spewing smoke—they emit only pure water vapor.

Nucor Steel buys water from the city and also collects rainwater on-site. The plant uses as much of the rainwater as possible, but heavy storms can fill up the storage tanks. When rainfall exceeds the on-site storage capacity, the excess water gets filtered and sent into Elliot Bay, the body of water just west of Seattle.

As a bar mill, Nucor's Seattle facility is in the business of producing rebar, the cylindrical steel bars used to reinforce concrete buildings. Each billet passes through a rolling machine that reheats the billet to glowing hot and squeezes the steel into a long cylindrical bar. The hot bar shoots rapidly out the rolling machine horizontally, where a cutting blade chops it into individual pieces that fall into a waiting bin. These pieces are rebar, ready to be bundled up and sold to fabricators who will then sell them to the construction industry.

The Seattle-area building boom provides Nucor a ready-made local market. As I drove from the Nucor steel plant back to my office, I passed a construction site for the light rail expansion due to finish in 2023. The aboveground tracks are built with dozens of concrete pillars, all of which will be reinforced with 100 percent recycled-steel rebar from Nucor.

Aluminum production

Aluminum is a relative latecomer to the collection of commercially produced metals, having not been discovered until the nineteenth century. Aluminum production is not nearly as efficient as iron production. Whereas magnetite contains 72 percent iron, it takes more than four tons of the source mineral bauxite to produce a ton of aluminum.

In addition to being one of the most energy-intensive metals to produce, aluminum production is also quite toxic. Residues from bauxite processing contain heavy metals that are present as contaminants, caustic byproducts (sodium hydroxide is added during processing to extract the aluminum metal), and radioactive waste.

The "red mud" dumped into pits near bauxite mines has a consistency that could make it attractive as a source of materials for building bricks. Unfortunately, the red mud contains significant levels of radioactive isotopes of radium and thorium. Red mud, therefore, can't be safely used in the construction industry, which is something that people had considered as a possible way to reuse this residue from mining.

Despite concerns about the consequences of aluminum mining, existing processes are relatively cost effective, making aluminum inexpensive. Aluminum is desirable as a construction material because it is light, with a good ratio of strength to weight, and easily formed into complex shapes. Reducing weight is critical for aircraft and also a good idea for motor vehicles. The lighter the car or truck, the easier it is to make it fuel efficient.

Aluminum is the most frequently recycled metal in the world. The popularity of aluminum recycling, covered more extensively in Chapter 6, is a direct result of the drawbacks of producing aluminum from mining bauxite.

Meanwhile, let's move on to the benefits and drawbacks of heavy metals.

What makes a metal heavy?

Discussion of contaminated water supplies often centers around the presence of heavy metals, among other contaminants. Heavy metals contain more protons in each atom than lighter metals. Elements on the periodic table are arranged in order of increasing atomic number, defined by the number of protons in each atom. A quick glance at the periodic table reveals that metals range considerably in atomic number. Lithium is the lightest metal, with atomic number 3. Lead, one of the elements that come to mind when thinking about heavy metals, has an atomic number of 82. Gold is nearby, with an atomic number of 79.

Heavy metals are not necessarily toxic—gold being an obvious example—but many of them are. Permits for solid waste disposal in the state of Washington require companies to comply with a vast array of requirements, including reporting on the metal content in their waste stream. They must include data on concentrations of the following metal contaminants: arsenic, barium, cadmium, chromium, copper, lead, mercury, molybdenum, nickel, selenium, and zinc. Not all these metals present the same degree of concern, and not all of them are heavy metals.

On a federal level, the presence of any of eight specific elements above certain threshold concentrations renders waste "hazardous" because of its toxicity. Hazardous waste cannot be discarded into landfills.

Many of the heaviest naturally occurring metallic elements—including radium, uranium, and polonium—are radioactive. Radioactive materials are health hazards, but they can also be used to improve health. For example, nuclear medicine for cancer treatment involves injecting a patient with radioactive tracers to identify the precise location of a tumor. In this case, the benefit of destroying the tumor outweighs the risks of exposure to the radioactive tracer.

Thankfully, however, knowledge of the dangers of radioactive elements has progressed sufficiently in the past century that safeguards are in place to limit the risk when these elements are used for beneficial purposes. The dangerous working conditions that occurred at the Radium Dial Corporation are unlikely to recur.

The focus here, however, is not addressing the proper use of radioactive elements or policies related to the handling of radioactive waste. We have plenty to discuss regarding the safety of lead, cadmium, and other nonradioactive, but toxic, metals.

Getting the lead out

Lead (Pb) is one of the heavy metals known to be toxic to humans, even in very small doses. It has been conclusively linked to mental retardation in those continually exposed to lead as children, through the paint on the walls of their homes and the water flowing through their pipes. Though children are the most susceptible because of their small size and growing brains and bodies, people of all ages can suffer ill effects from ingesting lead.

We as a society have not always been informed about the toxic nature of lead or been sufficiently concerned about it. My 1958 Encyclopedia Britannica, which I inherited from my grandparents and will keep even though my husband says the volumes make better paperweights than reference material, barely mentions toxicity in its lengthy entry on lead. It calls lead "one of the more important industrial metals." But the Ethyl Corporation knew that lead was toxic at least as early as the 1930s. Like other companies before and after it, the Ethyl Corporation suppressed the data implicating tetraethyl lead because it didn't like results that conflicted with its business plans.

It is somewhat ironic that ancient alchemists tried to turn lead into gold. All radioactive elements eventually decay to lead, so just waiting long enough will theoretically turn any radioactive substance into lead. Depending on the half-life—the time it takes for half of the atoms in a sample to decay—this process could take centuries or even millions of years. Turning lead into something else is even harder. Many barriers exist when attempting to replace lead in applications where its properties have proved useful for decades, if not centuries.

The ancient Romans made extensive use of lead. The chemical symbol Pb comes from the Latin "plumbum," which is also the sourcing of the word "plumbing." This is no coincidence. Romans used lead alloys to construct their water pipes. Today, newly constructed water pipes are made from copper or plastic, but our water systems are unfortunately far from lead-free (more on that later in this chapter).

Not only were the Romans unaware of the dangers of lead, they willingly consumed it. The lead acetate that used to be a common additive in twentieth-century paints was also known as lead sugar, because of a sweetening property it has that Romans took advantage of: they stored wine in lead vessels to make it taste better. These vessels probably contained lead in quantities sufficient to cause lead poisoning. I won't go into the controversies about whether lead poisoning brought about the fall of the Roman Empire. However, the concept of ingesting lead on purpose is strangely reminiscent of the late nineteenth and early twentieth centuries when people thought that radium, the "wonder element," was healthy.

Thinking about pewter

On a trip to Vancouver, British Columbia, while researching this book, I started thinking about pewter. I was browsing the gift shop at the Capilano Suspension Bridge when a collection of earrings caught my eye. Although I own plenty of earrings—at least twenty-five pairs—I decided I had to get the hummingbird set. They advertise being made from lead-free pewter and handcrafted in Canada, and the hummingbird is supposedly a symbol of good fortune. How could I not buy them?

I hadn't previously thought much about pewter, a metal alloy consisting primarily of tin. Modern pewter drinking vessels, at least those produced in Western countries, are free of the lead often found in ancient metal containers and have been for many decades. Britannia pewter, invented in England in the eighteenth century, is an alloy of tin, copper, and antimony and is harder than earlier pewter alloys that contained lead. Its hardness allows it to be rolled and formed into complex shapes rather than being cast into molds, reducing the cost of pewter items. Pewter for food usage today is based on Britannia pewter, containing at least 92 percent tin, 6–7.5 percent antimony, and the balance copper.

Companies that sell pewter mugs and tankards promote the material as being superior to glass or stainless steel for drinking beer. Pewter has been called "poor man's silver" because, while tin is less expensive than silver, pewter vessels have a similar shine to that of polished silver. Pewter has the advantage of not tarnishing like silver or potentially corroding like stainless steel. As for preferring pewter to glass for drinking beer? I'm not convinced.

Pewter jewelry, like pewter drinkware, contains antimony and copper to increase hardness and durability. The alloy remains soft enough to be formed into elaborate designs but hard enough not to be easily damaged. Only low grades of pewter for inexpensive jewelry contain lead, and these items are not made in the US or Canada. The lead-free claim on my hummingbird earrings, therefore, does not make them unusual.

What is lead good for?

Lead has many desirable properties. It is a relatively soft metal, although not quite as soft as the lanthanides (a subset of the rare earth elements, discussed later in this chapter), which can easily be cut with a table knife. Compared to structural metals like aluminum, lead is much easier to deform into complex shapes, even without heating above room temperature. Lead's softness is part of what made it so desirable for water pipes. Its low melting point also makes it easy to melt and pour into molds to create cast metal objects. Lead is present in high concentrations in several naturally occurring ores, making it inexpensive to extract and therefore much less costly than other commercial metals.

Because of its high atomic number, lead blocks radiation. This is why people wear lead aprons when getting medical X-rays so that parts of the body not being examined will not be exposed to damaging radiation. The lead is sealed inside the aprons and does not present a hazard in this application.

Lead has been phased out of certain products, notably gasoline and paint, because of concerns about toxicity. Tetraethyl lead used to be a standard additive in gasoline. It provided a valuable benefit of improving engine performance and reducing knocking. But data on dangerous lead exposure linked to gasoline eventually resulted in a push to remove the additive.

When I was growing up, gas stations offered regular, premium, and unleaded gasoline. My parents' 1967 Volvo took premium, a leaded type of gasoline, but our newer cars used unleaded. Although unleaded gasoline became available in the 1970s, the US did not ban tetraethyl lead until 1995. Japan was the first country to enact a ban, in 1986, but leaded gasoline didn't disappear from European and Chinese markets until 2000.

The largest use of lead today is in batteries, primarily for lead-acid batteries for vehicles. A typical car battery contains 10 kg (22 lb) of lead, while larger truck batteries require 13 kg (29 lb). This translates to more than eleven million metric tons of lead per year, just for vehicle batteries. The large batteries that power electric vehicles are lithium-ion batteries, which do not contain lead.

Solder: leaded or unleaded?

Solders used to connect dissimilar metals also include lead as a critical component. Although the total volume of lead in solders is much lower than that in batteries, the existence of lead poses similar health concerns. Solder joints may be relatively large, as in those used in plumbing, or so small that they aren't visible without a microscope, as in those used to connect computer chips to printed circuit boards. Lead is desirable in solders because it forms low-melting compounds that easily adhere to metal surfaces.

Eutectic tin-lead solder, comprised of 63 percent tin and 37 percent lead, was the standard solder for electronics for decades. The term "eutectic" refers to the composition that produces the lowest possible melting point for an alloy made from two or more metals. Just like a single metal, a eutectic has a fixed melting point, one that is lower than those of both the metals from which it is made. Tin melts at 232 degrees Celsius, and lead at 327, but eutectic tin-lead melts at 183, which happens to be just right for soldering chips onto circuit boards. After decades of working with the alloy, engineers had figured out the best temperature profile needed to create long-lasting solder joints.

In the 1990s, the European Union threw a wrench into the works when it proposed regulations aimed at eliminating six toxic materials from electronics manufacturing. Over the following decade, the industry had to figure out a way to eliminate lead, mercury, cadmium, hexavalent chromium, and several flame-retardant materials. The Restriction of Hazardous Substances directive, known as RoHS, originally became law in 2002 and has since undergone multiple revisions. When I first heard of RoHS, I recall people pronouncing the acronym like the name Ross, but "roe-hoss" seems to be more popular today.

Since 2006, manufacturers wanting to sell electrical and electronic equipment in the EU have had to comply with RoHS. One aspect of compliance meant getting rid of tin-lead solder. Although nonconformists like Joe Fjelstad (see interview) propose removing solder entirely, the commonly accepted approach is to use lead-free solders. These solders are made primarily from tin (Sn), with additions of silver (Ag) and copper (Cu), and are known as SAC alloys.

Simply put, SAC alloys don't work as well as eutectic tin-lead when it comes to soldering computer chips onto circuit boards. They melt at a higher temperature, typically 217–220 degrees Celsius. If the solder doesn't fully melt, it is impossible to create a reliable solder joint. As a consequence, the ovens used to melt the solder joints on circuit boards need to be set to higher temperatures. Ironically, ovens operating at a higher temperature consume more energy, which may have a greater negative environmental impact than continuing to use tin-lead solder. But the semiconductor industry didn't have a choice, and after fifteen years, manufacturers have learned how to work with SAC alloys and produce sufficiently reliable solder joints.

INTERVIEW Joe Fjelstad, Verdant Electronics

Joe Fjelstad is convinced that his quest to remove solder from electronics is something the semiconductor industry should embrace. He has long claimed that the way around restrictions on lead in solder is not to remove the lead from solder, but to remove the solder from the printed circuit board. His take on the effort to switch to lead-free solders is that the semiconductor industry has spent a billion dollars to solve a non-problem. But, despite Joe's twenty-year crusade, today's electronic devices are loaded with lead-free solder joints.

Joe likes to point out that he's never known anyone to get lead poisoning from tin-lead solder. What he means is that no one working in semiconductor manufacturing has been poisoned as a result of exposure to solder. Of course, he wasn't talking about e-waste incinerating facilities in Asia. Even when discussing e-waste, though, Joe claims that the solution is in educating people about how to process e-waste more safely rather than getting rid of toxic metals in the products. Sending electronics overseas to be disassembled by uneducated people without access to the necessary tools and safety equipment is, in Joe's words, either amoral or immoral.

Regardless of whether banning lead in solder made sense from a safety or environmental viewpoint, that's what happened. People from the Tin Research Institute, who had a vested interest in removing lead because the likely substitute alloys were more than 90 percent tin, convinced government officials in Europe to ban lead. The scientific data suggested waiting for a more thorough analysis, but the parliament went ahead. And what happened? For one thing, tin prices escalated.

People were understandably worried about the dangers of lead, but what about the unintended consequences of the metals used in lead-free solders? Joe points out that silver may seem benign, but it has antimicrobial properties. Self-cleaning fabrics are infiltrated with silver-containing compounds. The antimicrobial nature of silver, however, means that it kills microbes indiscriminately. It doesn't only attack undesirable microorganisms but may also destroy beneficial microbes in the soil. Therefore, it makes sense to ban waste contaminated with silver from landfills.

When semiconductor industry associations caricatured Joe as a modern-day Don Quixote in the 1990s, he wasn't exactly pleased but took heart that his message was getting people's attention, even if they thought his idea was absurd. Joe still believes that removing solder from most electronic devices is the right idea.

He could stand to make a lot of money if he sold licenses to use the alternative technology he invented. Solder in electronics is a market worth $100 billion per year, so replacing even 10 percent represents a substantial dollar value. But Joe, a semi-retired semiconductor industry veteran turned hiking enthusiast who can outpace hikers half his age, doesn't need the money. He is living comfortably in a small town east of Seattle, where natural beauty and mountains are just outside his door but the city is only a half-hour drive away if he times his travel right. At this point in his life, Joe would rather make a positive difference for future generations than accumulate more money. His brain is full of ideas, some of which may be crazy and others of which may help him add to his already impressive patent portfolio.

He believes that designers should expand their horizons beyond their preconceived notions. To this end, Joe created something called the Occam Prize. Competitors for the prize redesign one of their existing products using new constraints. Instead of soldering computer chips onto boards, chips are embedded into the board itself using a method Joe invented called the Occam Process. Joe's process is named after Occam's Razor, the concept that the simplest explanation of something is most likely correct.

Joe's opinion about cell phones reflects his belief in simple designs that build up a product from individual modules. Today's smartphones are overkill for many people's needs, according to Joe. His phone is a hand-me-down from his daughter, and he finds it to be completely satisfactory. Starting over from scratch could result in simpler modular phones that waste fewer resources while still including the functions that are necessary to communicate and do business in the twenty-first century.

Joe calls Bernard London's book *Ending the Depression Through Planned Obsolescence* an entertaining, provocative read. The book, published in 1932, is out of print and not available through normal channels, including my local public libraries, but Joe sent me a link to a digitized copy held at the University of Wisconsin. London lamented peoples' insistence on using items until they were worn out rather than replacing them with newer versions.

London spoke out in favor of planned obsolescence and wanted the government to mandate that consumer products like appliances come with expiration dates. Once items had expired, consumers would turn them in for a rebate on the sales tax they had paid when they bought the items. That didn't come to pass, but many industries adopted products that were "good enough" to function for a limited length of time. Products are no longer built to last generations. They are built to last only long enough to give the manufacturer time to release a new version. Joe and I are not especially pleased with this turn of events.

Lead in the water

I find it astounding that decades after we removed lead from gasoline and paint, and more than a decade since most solders became lead-free, there is still lead in the water supplies of many cities around the world. Lead pipes older than today's senior citizens, as well as copper pipes connected with tin-lead solder, still supply water to millions of people.

The Centers for Disease Control and Prevention (CDC) in the US provides guidance on its website regarding lead in water supplies. As the CDC points out, lead leaches into water supplies from solder connecting the pipes in buildings constructed before modern guidelines took effect, as well as from lead pipes in even older buildings.

In the US, the problem extends far beyond Flint, Michigan, where a change in the source of municipal water in 2015 made national headlines when an investigation revealed high levels of lead in the water coming from the new source. Water systems in all fifty states have shown excessive levels of lead. Concerned citizens can look up data on the EPA website or request a report from their local utilities and have the water in their homes tested, but these avenues may or may not yield reliable results.

The city of Redmond, Washington, has monitored lead levels in water annually since 1992, testing homes most likely to contain plumbing that uses tin-lead solder. Today's plumbing solders are alloys containing tin, silver, and copper. The 2016 Redmond report on lead states that ten out of 429 samples over the years have exceeded 15 ppb (parts per billion), the level that triggers action to address the contaminant. No samples in the past two years reported any measurable levels of lead. This is somewhat comforting.

Unfortunately, however, a reading of zero does not guarantee the plumbing is lead-free. Water needs to sit undisturbed in pipes for lead to leach out. It is possible that faucets that are rarely used may spew out contaminated water when the valve is opened.

After a pipe burst in my garage one winter, a casualty of weeks of sub-freezing temperatures, I hired a plumber to solder the pipes back together. He did not have an easy task since the broken section of pipe was nearly flush with the wooden beam behind it. The plumber had to solder pipes together in the proper configuration, thread them into a hole he cut in the drywall, and solder the whole assembly into place. This process got me to thinking about whether there is any lead in the pipes in my home. Since I live in a community where the oldest homes were built in 1991, the answer is probably no.

According to the latest water quality report from my city, "There is no detectable lead in any of the sources of Redmond drinking water." But the city does warn that older homes could have plumbing that is contaminated with lead. Lead-containing solders were not banned nationwide until 1986, with the passage of amendments to the Safe Drinking Water Act. We can thank the EPA for putting in regulations limiting toxic substances in the water we drink and the air we breathe.

One piece of advice for avoiding lead poisoning is to run cold water taps for at least thirty seconds before drinking or cooking with the water just in case. I remember being told decades ago to fill cooking pots with cold water from the tap, not hot water, even if I were going to boil the water. The reason was to minimize the chance of lead contamination, since hot water accelerates any possible leaching of toxins. Since my parents' house was built in the 1960s, this was probably good advice.

I am fairly confident that my water at home is safe. Unfortunately, the citizens of Flint, Michigan, have no such confidence, nor should they.

Progress has been made in Flint. As of January 2017, around 600 water pipes had been replaced, which may sound good except that almost 30,000 lead pipes remain. Residents no longer get water from the contaminated Flint River, and the city has added corrosion inhibitors to limit the amount of lead that leaches into the water supply, but the water is still not safe to drink without filtration, and many don't trust the filtration systems. A year after the media publicized the crisis, donations that poured in had slowed to a trickle, and the residents of Flint were still drinking bottled water and likely will need to rely on it for the foreseeable future. Extensive sales of bottled water may be good news for bottled water suppliers, but it's not a good long-term solution.

General Motors, which had clean water for its industrial use in Flint while the residents of Flint suffered from lead-tainted water, expanded its water bottle collection program to include millions of bottles from the Flint community. The bottles are finding new life as fleece used in engine covers and air filters for GM cars. This is a nice example of material reuse, but the fleece is used in another product that makes a more compelling story.

GM has donated fleece to an organization called The Empowerment Plan, which is using it to make 6,500 coats for the homeless. These coats transform into sleeping bags, but that is not all that makes them especially valuable. The Empowerment Plan employs previously homeless people to sew the coats, teaching them skills they can use to pave their way toward more lucrative careers. GM has also donated a significant amount of cash to the organization.

While GM's programs have a feel-good vibe and do help local residents, they don't do anything to solve the national and global water safety crisis. Much larger infusions of money will be needed to accomplish that. In the US alone, the price tag is on the order of hundreds of billions of dollars to ensure that all Americans have safe drinking water. Replacing miles of water pipes is an expensive undertaking, which is probably why proposed new regulations from the EPA require removing lead service lines within twenty years. A new generation of children will grow up drinking contaminated water during those decades.

As of early 2018, two years after the Flint water crisis, the EPA was working on changes to the Lead and Copper Rule (LCR). The rule states that governments must take action if more than 10 percent of water samples exceed the allowable level of 15 ppb lead. Possible actions include improving corrosion control or replacing lead pipes. The proposed new rules would lower the level of lead concentration requiring action, in addition to requiring all lead pipes to be replaced.

As this book goes to press, the citizens of Flint are still receiving free bottled water. They have recently been granted the ability to sue the state of Michigan over its handling of water supplies. Money can't bring their children back to health, as lead poisoning is irreversible, but at least it can keep them afloat financially. Meanwhile, residents of other communities are still drinking and cooking with lead-laced tap water, in many cases without knowing whether their water supplies are safe.

Unlike some other contaminants, lead doesn't affect the look, taste, or smell of water. That is part of what makes it so insidious. If people could identify the presence of lead easily, the problem might have been taken care of long ago.

The problem with demolition

Professor of history Andrew Highsmith called his 2015 book about the history of Flint, Michigan, *Demolition Means Progress*. The book, published before the city's water crisis unfolded, focuses on the changing demographics of Flint during the twentieth century and racial injustice. Highsmith goes into a level of detail that is of greatest interest to people who grew up in Flint, either on the white or the black side of town, and is not quite as fascinating to those who have never been to the state of Michigan.

I find Highsmith's book title ironic because demolition of old buildings poses a serious risk of lead contamination. Cities have laws in place that are supposed to ensure that neither workers nor nearby residents are exposed to lead or asbestos when homes and businesses are torn down, but these rules are not always followed.

In Portland, Oregon, a city that prides itself on being progressive, a 2017 investigation found that many developers were certifying that homes were free of lead-based paint when that was not the case. A 2015 city law requires that demolition crews remove any suspicious siding, doors, or windows before demolishing the building. Developers checked off the box saying that no lead was present, even on homes built early in the twentieth century. Though the homes certainly would have been repainted with lead-free paint in the past decade or two, it is likely that residue from old paint remained. In some cases, homes with documented presence of lead were demolished without removing any contaminated elements.

The law obviously wasn't working to protect the citizens of Portland. A state program took effect in January 2018, supposedly giving cities more power to enforce proper precautions during demolition. Portland responded with a new ordinance requiring removal of all non-load-bearing painted materials from houses built before 1978 before demolishing the rest of the structure. Will the ordinance achieve better results? That remains to be seen.

▓ Not-so-rare earth metals

Consumer electronics such as smartphones and laptop computers contain not only toxic metals like lead and cadmium but also a variety of rare earth metals. Rare earth elements are primarily those that appear at the bottom of the periodic table—the lanthanide series that is separate from the rest of the table, plus the transition metals scandium and yttrium.

Certain rare earth elements are used in extremely small quantities in consumer electronics but are nonetheless critical to the functioning of the components inside. They help produce colors in the screens of smartphones and computers and create the magnets inside speakers and microphones. Many of these elements are also useful in the nuclear power industry, as well as in electric vehicles and wind turbines. The future of power and communications depends on rare earth elements.

Despite what the term "rare earth" implies, these elements are not rare. They exist in ores that are fairly common in the Earth's crust, but they are hard to extract compared to metals like iron, copper, or even aluminum. The various rare earth elements are difficult to separate from one another chemically and are very reactive. Trade policies have exacerbated the difficulty in obtaining the rare earth elements that manufacturers need. Most of the mines where these elements can be found are in China, a country that set policies designed to artificially control the prices and maintain a monopoly.

Chinese crackdowns on illegal and dangerous mining operations, a new approach after years of minimal regulation, are changing the situation. Prices are increasing to reflect the true costs of running mining operations, including immense cleanup costs for sites contaminated with radioactive thorium. The good news is that future mining operations in China will place a greater emphasis on safety and proper waste disposal. The bad news is the risk of escalating prices and a shortage of important minerals.

Segment of periodic table

Seven rare earth metals (those shaded below plus yttrium) are used in electronics

Lathanides

57	58	59	60	61	62	63	64	65	66	67	68	69	70	71
La	Ce	Pr	Nd	Pm	Sm	Eu	Gd	Tb	Dy	Ho	Er	Tm	Yb	Lu

▢ Used in electronics

Countries other than China, including Australia and Canada, are developing sources of mined rare earth elements. A more diverse global supply will reduce the risk of shortages, but increased mining is not the best answer from an environmental viewpoint.

Improved recycling of e-waste presents a huge, mostly unexplored, opportunity for those looking for efficient sources of raw materials. Better e-waste recycling holds the promise of both reducing worker exposure to toxic metals and recovering useful metals without mining.

Electronics currently in use are not the only potential source of e-waste. Landfills contain a wealth of metals locked up in discarded cell phones and computers. The industry of urban mining, where metals are extracted from landfills instead of from mines, may reduce the need to discover more sources of metallic ores. Chapter 7 delves further into e-waste problems and solutions.

PART III

Rethinking Manufacturing

CHAPTER 6

Reduce, Reuse, Recycle

"We love it when people scrap stuff, and they love us because we can manage it, but if you're going to truly look at all those costs…"
—*Smokey Peck, Interwest Paper*

"You can't accidentally get 95 percent of the way toward zero waste to landfill."
—*Jenna Arkin, Earth Friendly Products*

The recycling landscape

How can our society use less material? The "reduce, reuse, recycle" mantra shows the way. All of the options in the diagram on the next page represent possible strategies, which I describe briefly here and delve into in greater depth later in the chapter.

Improve product design to use less raw material. Consider the evolution of beverage cans. Aluminum cans for beer and soft drinks were first introduced in 1959, but it took a few decades to completely replace steel. During this time, manufacturers replaced virgin aluminum with recycled aluminum and redesigned the can to use less material. Early versions required 85 grams of aluminum per can. By reducing the thickness of the can body and shrinking the lid, engineers were able to create a perfectly functional can with less than 13 grams of aluminum.

Possible strategies to reduce materials use

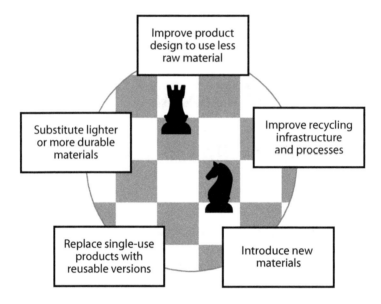

Substitute lighter or more durable materials. Replacing steel with aluminum or switching from metal or glass to plastic reduces weight, but this approach requires caution to avoid creating more waste or using more energy. A thorough analysis needs to consider the resources required to produce the raw materials, make the product, ship the product, and dispose of it at the end of its life cycle.

Improve recycling infrastructure and processes. Recycling rates improve when collection is easier and more convenient for residents and business owners. Advances in recycling technology increase the variety of materials that can be economically recycled, and policies such as container deposits encourage consumers to return cans and bottles to stores.

Replace single-use products with reusable versions. Reusable packaging harkens back to a time before inexpensive disposable packaging became readily available. Reversing habits in the other direction will not be easy, but it is possible and is already happening.

Introduce new materials. Scientists are continually working to develop new materials and chemicals that can provide a safer or less wasteful substitute for those in use today.

Recycling alone does not solve the problem of excessive materials production and waste, but it does serve as an important piece of the puzzle. This chapter starts by explaining why recycling is valuable, looking at the energy needed to produce various materials.

Not all recycling processes are equally effective, however, which is why I delve into the challenges of recycling metals, plastics, and other types of materials. The interviews in this chapter feature two perspectives on these challenges, one from a long-standing recycling facility in Utah and another from a startup in Colorado creating a new way to recycle scrap carbon-fiber composites.

Reasons to recycle

The motivations for recycling seem obvious: reduce carbon footprint, trash, and pollution.

Emissions. Recycling reduces the carbon footprint of manufacturing by reducing the carbon emissions associated with producing raw materials. Metals or plastics made from recycled materials take less energy to produce than those made from virgin materials extracted from the Earth.

Trash. Recycling can result in less trash cluttering up our streets and waterways. Deposit systems in which consumers get cash back by returning cans or bottles incent people to return these items rather than discard them, hence reducing trash. Depositing cardboard and plastic packaging into recycling bins diverts these materials from landfills, and strategically placed recycling bins may increase the rate of recycling.

Pollution. Recycling ideally reduces pollution in two ways. It extends the lifespan of landfills and delays the need to burn trash when landfills run out of space. Increased recycling of products should lead to reduced raw materials production, eliminating the toxic byproducts of producing those materials. That doesn't happen to as great an extent as people assume because materials sent for recycling are not always properly recycled.

Recycling rates range from nearly zero for plastics in the developing world to 80 percent or higher for metals in some US cities, but low rates are the norm. Why is so little material recycled? There are many factors at play, from the economics and technology of recycling to the difficulty in changing human behavior.

Energy cost of various materials, gigajoules per ton

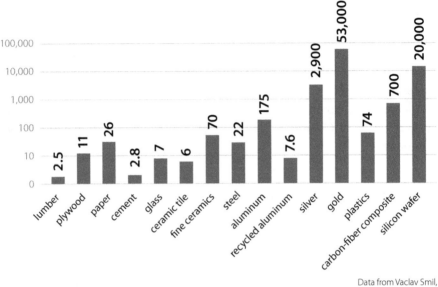

Data from Vaclav Smil,
Making the Modern World

The energy cost of materials

The energy cost of producing a ton of material varies greatly depending on the material in question. This energy is measured in units of gigajoules (GJ), or billions of joules, and includes all the heat needed to produce the material, starting from harvesting or extracting it from the Earth through processing it into a material that can be used to build a product.

Energy costs range from as low as 1.5 GJ per ton for lumber to 53,000 GJ per ton of gold. This, by the way, is the reason gold is so expensive. Gold is present in such minute quantities in mineral deposits that many tons of rock need to be mined and broken up to yield an ounce of gold.

The graph shows how expensive metals and plastics are, regarding the energy required to produce them, compared to natural materials that require much less processing before use. Because the vertical axis of the graph is logarithmic scale, the differences are greater than they appear at first glance. Gold takes 1,000 times more energy to produce per ton than the average plastic. Silver is much less costly to mine than gold but is still energy-intensive, at 2,900 GJ/ton.

Two ways to extract an ounce of gold

2–90 tons
of gold ore

0.25 tons
(1,000 phones)

Improving production methods can help reduce energy consumption. The key example of success in this area is for steel. In 1950, it required around 60 GJ to produce a ton of steel from iron ore. This value is now down to 20 GJ, achieved by developing more efficient methods of producing steel.

Producing metal from recycled scrap instead of mined ore reduces energy consumption dramatically, especially for aluminum. The effect is not as great for steel, but making steel from scrap steel is still substantially more energy-efficient than making it from iron ore.

Gold mining is incredibly inefficient, but because gold is seen as desirable, it can fetch an open market price that makes it economically worth the effort to extract it from tons of ore. What if there were a source of gold that required crushing much less material to produce every ounce? There is. An object that people around the world use every day can provide an impressively efficient source of gold.

An average cell phone contains approximately 0.03 grams of gold. An ounce is about 28 grams. This means that it is technically possible to recover an ounce of gold from fewer than 1,000 phones. Assuming each phone weighs half a pound, this translates to extracting an ounce of gold from less than a quarter of a ton of phones. The weight of the printed circuit boards inside the phones that contain the gold is even lower. For perspective, data from Barrick Gold showed that, in the first quarter of 2013, the company mined between 2 and 91 tons of ore to produce each ounce of gold.

Conventional e-waste recycling processes are not 100 percent efficient, so the actual recovery rate is lower than an ounce per 1,000 phones. Still, the concentration of gold in cell phones is clearly much greater than that in mines. Chapter 7 dives more deeply into the technology and economics of e-waste recycling.

The recycling process

Many people don't know what happens when they toss items into a recycling bin, nor do they necessarily understand which materials are recyclable. This section will clear up some of that confusion.

What is recyclable?

Recycling facilities in the US pick up paper, metal, and plastics, but figuring out exactly which items in each category belong in a recycling bin is not straightforward.

People are often surprised by what is and isn't recyclable. For example, store receipts made from thermal paper aren't recyclable. The paper is coated with bisphenol A (BPA) or bisphenol S (BPS), the same toxic additives that caused health alerts for reusable plastic water bottles. Before I watched a webinar on recycling, I wasn't aware of the coatings and had been unknowingly contaminating my recycling bin. I imagine that a lot of people are equally ignorant.

Paper coffee cups are not usually recyclable (nor compostable) because of the polyethylene coating on the inside. It performs a valuable function—keeping the hot liquid inside the cup from leaking through the paper—but it causes problems for recycling since it can't be easily separated from the rest of the cup, and the plastic clogs the machinery used to recycle paper. As of 2017, a few paper recycling mills are able to process plastic-coated paper by separating the lining from the paper cup.

The organization Stand.earth, which started as ForestEthics and whose initial efforts focused on protecting forests from the logging of 1,000-year-old trees, is now working on multiple environmental campaigns. Stand.earth published a report in 2017 focusing on Starbucks coffee cups. Stand.earth is campaigning for Starbucks to source fully recyclable cups, but as of 2018, this is still a work in progress.

If there were an easy answer, I believe that Starbucks would have done it. The company is mindful of its impact on the environment and agrees that making its cups recyclable is a good idea. But simply removing the plastic lining won't work. That approach creates a cup that doesn't serve its intended purpose. Hot coffee would soak through the cup, causing more problems than it solves.

In 2016, Starbucks worked with the company Frugalpac to test out its recyclable cups. The concept was to produce cups where the plastic lining is more loosely connected to the paper and can be separated at a recycling plant.

Frugalpac claims that its cups can be recycled at any paper recycling facility in the UK. So far, the pilot project doesn't seem to have resulted in widespread adoption.

Certain items, such as plain paper and aluminum cans, are universally recyclable in the US. Others, such as thermal paper and lined coffee cups, cannot be commercially recycled at all. Many materials and products, however, fall into a gray area. Regulations vary from place to place depending on existing technology and practices. Something that is recyclable in one city may not be recyclable in an adjoining city in the same metropolitan region.

For example, before 2019, residents in Redmond, Washington were supposed to remove caps from plastic water bottles before tossing them into the recycling bin, but in adjoining Bellevue, the caps were to stay on, firmly attached to the bottles. It complicates matters when residential and commercial recycling in the same city follow different rules. Items that are recyclable at home are not recyclable at work, and vice versa.

Single-stream or dual-stream

The reason for the variability in recycling rules from city to city lies in differences between processes, equipment, and budgets at various recycling facilities, also known as material recovery facilities. This variation starts at the collection step before materials even get to a recycling facility. Collection at the curbside or in commercial dumpsters can be either single-stream, in which people dump all their recyclables into one bin, or multi-stream, in which some degree of sorting takes place during collection. Typical dual-stream processes differentiate between paper and all other recyclables.

When I moved to San Jose, California, in the mid-1990s, homeowners were given three plastic recycling bins. In this triple-stream process, one bin was for paper, one for plastic, and one for metal. Local hardware stores sold convenient carts on wheels that held all three bins, making it easier to get all that recycled material to the curbside. At some point in the early 2000s, the region transitioned to a single large bin for all recyclables, a huge garbage can on wheels. It made recycling easier.

The single-stream approach promotes increased recycling rates, which is why many cities have migrated to this type of collection. But easier recycling comes at the expense of a less efficient process once the materials reach a recycling facility. More varied contents on the trucks that transport recyclables to recycling facilities for sorting and processing translates to a greater number of machines required to separate out the various materials. It takes energy to run these machines, reducing the energy savings of producing products from recycled materials rather than virgin materials. It also takes time, both to run the machines and to hand sort to remove items that don't belong in the recycling stream. All this reduces the value of the recyclables.

Contamination is also greater in facilities that use single-stream collection. Reducing contamination to desirable levels, 5 percent or less, requires an investment in more staff to hand sort materials and a willingness to run conveyor belts at a slower speed. This makes the process more effective, but also more expensive.

A dual-stream system can achieve similar contamination levels as a single-stream system but at a lower cost. For this reason, many in the recycling industry are proponents of dual-stream recycling.

Once materials arrive at a material recovery facility for single-stream or dual-stream recycling, they go through the following basic steps:

1. Trucks dump materials into a holding area.

2. Materials move onto feeders and conveyor belts.

3. Staff hand sort to remove large items that will jam equipment. These items typically go to a different facility.

4. Materials are separated into categories: paper, cardboard, plastic, ferrous metals (iron and steel), aluminum, etc. A variety of equipment automates the sorting process.

5. Each separate stream of materials is compacted into bales for further processing, usually at a separate facility. The materials undergo either chemical or mechanical recycling (see page 123), depending on the material and the technology available.

INTERVIEW   Smokey Peck, Interwest Paper

Recycling is alive and well in Salt Lake City, Utah. I talked with Smokey Peck, president of the recycling company Interwest Paper, who has been involved with recycling for decades. Prior to Interwest, he worked for recycling giant Waste Management for nineteen years, the last ten of those running one of their facilities in Salt Lake City. Smokey started working at Interwest in 2003, and in 2005 he bought out the previous owner. He also serves on the board of P3 Utah, a nonprofit organization based in Salt Lake City that encourages triple-bottom-line practices, in which companies consider the three Ps—profit, people, and planet—when making business decisions.

Interwest Paper started back in 1978, before the advent of curbside recycling for residential customers or on-site recycling for commercial customers. The company's primary business today is focused on commercial recycling. They serve as a distributor for recycling equipment, such as baling machines that compress single-stream waste. Depending on the volume of material a company needs to recycle every month, it can be more cost-effective to buy a baler than to send out unbaled materials. Interwest also processes waste at its own facility and sells the recycled material for reuse.

Interwest does collect e-waste, which it sends to a local processing facility. That facility extracts the precious metals from circuit boards but returns the plastic shells—outer cases from computers, monitors, and other electronic equipment—to Interwest. These cases become part of Interwest's plastic recycling stream.

Interwest requires its customers to pre-sort materials, since it processes only single-material, relatively uncontaminated waste.

Smokey told me about a local customer whose parent company was based in Europe, where businesses are subject to strict zero-waste-to-landfill regulations. All waste needed to be either recycled or burned for energy. He worked with them to meet the requirements.

Smokey doesn't use the term "lean," but he has embraced the concept. He understands how inventory control can help manage a recycling stream. Smokey has seen firsthand how it's a lot harder to create zero waste when a company is ordering more materials than they need or making more products than they can sell.

Interwest works with a company called Packsize that provides box-making machines. Flat corrugated cardboard goes in, the user specifies the desired box size, and boxes come out, perfectly sized to ship products. Companies don't have to pre-order shipping boxes in many different sizes since they can quickly build just as many as they need. This avoids the waste inherent in ordering thousands of boxes, which then go unused when a company changes its products and needs a different size of shipping box.

Smokey is a huge proponent of multi-stream recycling. Interwest processes primarily paper, glass, and plastic. If customers send in mixed waste, they will be charged a surplus fee. Incoming waste that can't be easily separated into pure single-material streams is directed to the waste-to-energy process. Customers have a financial incentive to provide the most efficiently processed waste.

In Salt Lake City, recycling facilities accept disposable water bottles along with their lids. Smokey said that many people are not aware that the lids and bottles are made from different materials. In the Interwest process, the lids, which are lower density than the bottles, float during the washing step and can be easily separated from the bottles before mechanical grinding.

Smokey keeps tabs on his customers. When he noticed that a regular customer was sending him less cardboard, he reached out to make sure they weren't throwing the cardboard away or losing business. They immediately called back and said that Smokey validated their cost savings approach. They were selling just as many products but using less packaging.

While Salt Lake City has a well-developed recycling infrastructure, composting is relatively new there. Green waste collection is now available, mostly for collecting excess wood and tree limbs, but some people are composting food waste. Momentum Glass in Utah collects both glass and food waste from restaurants and grocery stores.

Smokey is proud that Interwest provides clean recycled material, a commodity that is becoming more valuable as China is retreating from its role as global trash collector and processor. He realizes that encouraging recycling and embracing sustainable practices requires a mindset that has not been prevalent in his region.

Some years ago, Smokey was at a meeting at the Utah state capitol regarding curbside recycling. One of the representatives stood up and said he was not going to force his constituents to participate in such a program. Smokey explained how recycling would help some of those people financially. They would avoid the extra fee they were being charged for having two garbage cans. He further explained that cities are motivated to charge residents less for a recycling can than for a trash can because by reducing the amount of garbage, it prolongs the life of a landfill and saves money in the long term. In the end, the state representative relented.

Improved recycling practices can spread to new regions, but those promoting them will only succeed if they educate everyone involved, from state and local governments to citizens.

Metal recycling

Metals are one of the easiest categories of materials to recycle. The relatively high cost of virgin materials in terms of both dollar value and energy cost per pound provide an incentive to recycle various metals.

The most cost-efficient way to recycle metals is to do so where metal products are manufactured. Such recycling is common practice. As my plant tour with Nucor Steel (Chapter 5) demonstrated, steelmaking plants in the US incorporate recycling throughout their facilities.

Machine shops can either sweep metal shavings into a trash bin or save them. If the floor is kept clean and areas for machining different types of metal are separated, it is easy to create a high-purity supply of metal shavings that can be sold for remelting into new blocks or bars of metal.

Recycling products made from metal is cost-effective as well, especially for steel and aluminum. Metal isn't terribly difficult to separate from the rest of the recycling stream, even for single-stream systems. Magnets can easily pull out ferrous metals like iron and steel, since they are magnetic.

An eddy current separator, a machine with a magnetic rotor that spins at high speed, is used to filter out other metals after the steel is out of the way. The rotor creates an electric current in anything conductive, such as aluminum cans or scrap pieces of metal, that passes over the rotor. This current produces a magnetic field in the opposite direction from the field of the rotor. Much like two magnets with opposite poles repel each other, the force pushes the metal bits away from the rotor and into a bin. Materials that aren't electrically conductive, such as plastic, simply pass over the rotor and drop, via gravity, into a separate bin.

Eighteen kids in a VW bus

Aluminum is the most heavily recycled material in the world. More products are made from recycled aluminum than from virgin aluminum. As the data on the energy cost of materials show (see the graph on page 110), the reason is obvious.

I have fond memories of my first foray into aluminum recycling. When I was in elementary school in San Diego, seamless aluminum cans were newly recyclable. The going rate for empty aluminum cans was seventeen cents per pound. Each can contained a lot more aluminum that today's soda cans, so it look less time to collect a pound of cans than it would now.

My elementary school started an annual contest, rewarding the classroom that brought in the largest number of cans. Although Mr. Riley's fifth/sixth grade class was small, his class won every year because of Mr. Riley's unique strategy. He took us on a field trip to the beach to collect cans. All eighteen of us loaded into his VW Bus—this was in the days before seatbelt laws—and, armed with giant trash bags, gathered hundreds of discarded cans to bring back to school.

I remember that we had to examine the cans carefully and only take the aluminum ones. The steel cans had a telltale seam on the side, so we could distinguish them fairly easily. It surprises me that although several soft drink companies started producing aluminum cans in the 1960s, it wasn't until 1996 that steel cans were entirely phased out in the US. I shouldn't be surprised, though. Changing an industry takes time.

Much of the aluminum that has been extracted since the beginning of the twentieth century is still in use today, thanks to the ability of aluminum to be recycled over and over. There are limits, however, especially for specialty alloys that contain a variety of other elements. Refining these alloys for recycling requires separating out the various metals, which consumes time and energy and makes recycling less efficient.

As aluminum alloys become stronger and lighter, they unfortunately become more expensive to recycle. Even so, metals remain much easier to recycle than plastics.

The challenge of recycling plastics

Plastic's durability, which makes it desirable during use, is why disposal of plastic products is creating a growing environmental disaster. Plastic materials last a century or more, far longer than the useful lifespan of a plastic product.

Many plastics are recyclable, but recycling rates are low. Of the estimated 8.3 billion tons of plastic produced since the early twentieth century, 6.3 billion tons have become waste. Most discarded plastic in the US ends up in landfills. The US buries 80,000 tons of plastic in landfills every day. Much of the remaining plastic produced worldwide is still in use, or sitting unused in homes, garages, and commercial buildings. A relatively small amount—less than 10 percent—has been recycled.

Some countries do not have an infrastructure set up for recycling, which poses additional challenges (see the discussion of plastic trash in Chapter 4). But even in North America and Europe, where recycling is well established, several factors conspire to limit the recycling of plastics.

Economics. Compared to glass and metal, plastics are relatively low-value materials. It is often less expensive to throw them away and buy new raw materials than to recycle. Compared to aluminum, the difference in energy required to produce plastic from virgin materials instead of recycled materials is much smaller, lowering the incentive to recycle.

Diversity of plastics. Plastics form a diverse waste stream made up of many dissimilar materials that cannot easily be separated, especially if plastics are embedded in products made from layers of different organic and inorganic materials.

Confusing messaging. Regulations regarding what types of plastics and plastic objects can and cannot be recycled vary tremendously from place to place. Citizens are confused about what to toss in a recycling bin and are more likely to discard plastic into the trash than attempt to recycle it.

Plastic packaging makes up the largest component of the plastics waste stream. These are products designed for single use, as opposed to durable goods made out of plastic designed to last many years. One way to reduce waste is by reducing the use of excess packaging of consumer items. This is certainly possible and is a worthwhile goal.

There is certainly opportunity to reduce the amount of packaging being used without compromising the ability to safely ship products around the world. Recent years have seen a resurgence of interest in reducing disposable packaging. Even companies that make disposable packaging are getting on board to reduce the amount of plastic used per unit of product packaged.

Still, packaging is not going away. Disposable packaging fills a real need. It protects products during shipping while minimizing excess weight. In the health care field, disposable packaging guarantees sterility of medical instruments. The risk of contamination and infection is a greater concern than the packaging waste. Even in a hospital setting, however, it is possible to set up systems that encourage plastic recycling.

Numbered plastics

Plastic packaging containers are often labeled with a number from 1 to 7. The website for Earth911, an NGO that promotes recycling, includes the following statement: "The number on your plastic indicates what it's made of, but does not guarantee recyclability. Please explore these listings further before you recycle." Earth911 maintains a comprehensive database of recycling policies throughout the US, where visitors can look up a specific item and enter their ZIP code to learn whether the item is recyclable where they live and, if so, how to recycle it. For example, when I look up number 5 plastic bottles into the Earth911 site it brings up a link to my county's recycling program and a list of more than sixty items that I can recycle curbside.

Recycling facilities typically take products labeled 1, 2, 5, and sometimes 6. Some cities or counties group products by shape in addition to material because that approach works better with their sorting technology.

Even the best-designed recycling facilities manage a waste stream made up of at least a handful of different plastic materials. Because of confusion over what to toss into the recycling bin, plastic and nonplastic contaminants abound. Some contaminants are relatively easy to separate. Steps in which materials are sorted by density, for example, will quickly filter out materials that are much denser than plastics. But many plastic materials have very similar density, and unwanted plastics contaminate the recycling stream for recyclable plastics.

Some types of plastic packaging are easier to recycle than others. Those with toxic additives pose special problems, but even the shape and size of plastic packaging items plays a role. The section that follows explains the meaning behind the numbered labels on plastic products (see diagram).

1. PET/PETE. Water bottles made from polyethylene terephthalate (PET) are the most successfully recycled plastic packaging product, with a recycling rate of around 25 percent. Grinding up PET bottles and remelting them to create stock to produce more bottles reduces the energy required to produce the same number of bottles by 60–80 percent. But the presence of contaminants (see section below on PVC) can make the recycling process less effective.

2. HDPE. High-density polyethylene (HDPE) is used for milk jugs, bottles of household cleaners, and durable goods such as storage containers and furniture. It can be easily recycled into a variety of products, including drainage pipes and plastic lumber as well as the same types of containers that are made from virgin HDPE.

Plastic packaging materials by number
Curbside recycling typically accepts types 1, 2, and 5

PETE   HDPE   V   LDPE   PP   PS   OTHER

3. *PVC.* The "V" in the label stands for vinyl, but the primary polymer of concern is polyvinyl chloride (PVC). Curbside recycling programs do not want PVC mixed in with other recyclables. PVC causes problems with recycling because it is difficult to separate from other plastics. The presence of a single PVC bottle amongst a batch of 10,000 PET bottles being melted for recycling will ruin the melt. The acids in the PVC break down the PET. The result is a yellowish and brittle material, whose poor strength and unsightly appearance make it unsuitable for reuse. Because of these types of difficulties, as well as concerns about toxicity, consumer product companies are moving away from PVC. Unilever, for example, has removed PVC entirely from its packaging.

4. *LDPE.* Low-density polyethylene (LDPE), the material from which plastic grocery bags are made, is especially troubling because it is difficult to recycle. Many recycling facilities do not want to process LDPE because the material clogs up their machinery, and they have no end market for selling it. Despite being told not to discard plastic bags into recycling bins, lots of individuals and businesses in the US and Europe are doing just that, creating a headache for recyclers. Given the lightweight nature of LDPE products, these are the items most likely to escape the recycling or trash systems and become pollution.

5. *Polypropylene (PP).* Some polypropylene packaging, such as yogurt and ketchup containers, forms a desirable element in the recycling stream. These containers can be recycled into many products, including brooms, rakes, and storage bins. Lids and straws, however, are not as easily recycled, because their size makes it harder to separate them from other recyclables. Bans on plastic straws are picking up momentum as cities move to eliminate this source of waste.

6. *Polystyrene (PS).* Polystyrene most often appears in its expanded form. Expanded polystyrene (EPS), often referred to as Styrofoam, is used in egg cartons, meat trays, hot beverage cups, clamshell packaging for takeout foods, and packing "peanuts" that protect items being shipped. This material can theoretically be recycled but it usually isn't. Especially for food usage, EPS is often contaminated with food, which is only part of the problem. The other problem is that the material is very bulky for its weight, due to the air injected into it when the material is manufactured. As a result, the collection and transportation costs are high compared to the value of the material being collected.

Some cities have enacted bans on EPS for food use. Such bans exist in Washington, DC; Minneapolis; San Francisco; Oakland, California; Portland,

Oregon; Albany, New York; and Seattle. In response, restaurants have been replacing EPS with PET, polypropylene, or occasionally even polylactic acid materials. Paper or cardboard are also options. McDonald's got rid of its Styrofoam clamshells for packing burgers in 1990 and replaced them with cardboard ones. Unfortunately, their action did not result in a cascading trend in the fast-food industry.

7. *Other.* This category includes polycarbonates, acrylics, and nylon. These materials are more commonly used in durable goods rather than disposable packaging and aren't usually recyclable at standard recycling facilities.

Sorting technology: plastics recycling

Once the plastics are separated from paper and metal, various techniques exist to further sort plastics into specific materials, creating separate streams for PET, HDPE, polypropylene, and other plastics. Technology for sorting plastics to be recycled falls into one of three basic categories: optical sorting, image recognition, and markers.

In optical sorting, near-infrared spectroscopy remains the industry-standard method. Near-infrared spectroscopy analyzes the reflection from an illuminated piece of plastic to identify the type and grade of polymer, and state-of-the-art machines achieve nearly 100 percent accuracy. Each machine identifies one specific polymer to separate, though, so a recycling facility needs quite a few machines to sort all the materials they receive. This gets very expensive.

Image recognition involves automatically recognizing items by their shape or size. The problem here is that some containers arrive crushed or deformed, making it difficult for the machine to distinguish one from another. An ideal image recognition system might even be able to identify a brand by reading a logo, but this level of sophistication doesn't yet exist.

Brand identification would be helpful, though, especially if the system collected data on the number of different specific packages recycled and relayed that information back to the companies whose brands are being processed. Such a system might encourage brands to promote recycling of their products, competing against each other and increasing overall recycling rates.

The next level of sorting technology relies on bar codes or invisible chemical markers that machines can read. Patents exist to cover chemical markings and detection systems, but no commercial products for the recycling industry currently use this technology. If such products were developed, they could replace the near-infrared machines that are used for optical sorting.

The Polymark Project in the EU developed a version of chemical marker technology specifically designed to sort PET into categories of food-contact packaging and non-food-contact packaging. EU regulations stating that plastics from nonfood applications could not be recycled for food-contact use motivated the research project. The Polymark consortium, which issued a final report on the Polymark Project in 2018, screened hundreds of possible chemical markers. They built a prototype industrial-scale sorting machine and tested it with marked and standard PET bottles.

Toward higher-quality recycled plastics

Even with advances in sorting technology, sorting will probably never be 100 percent accurate. It's also hard to remove all contaminants even if materials are properly sorted. Therefore, it's also important to improve the rest of the recycling process to create higher-quality recycled plastics. As mentioned earlier, once material recovery facilities sort incoming materials, they compact them into bales for further processing. The next step for plastics is either mechanical or chemical recycling.

Mechanical recycling breaks the plastic into tiny pieces but keeps the polymer itself intact. This allows the recycling process to retain the highest amount of the material's value. This is especially true for closed-loop recycling, in which a material is recycled into the same type of object as that made from the virgin material. For example, used PET bottles would be recycled to make new PET bottles. The only way that quality is lost in this type of process is through contamination, which occurs when polymers that aren't supposed to be in the mix get in there. Contamination standards are strict. Batches of PET with more than 100 ppm (0.01 percent) of foreign particles aren't suitable for recycling into new bottles. Improved sorting and cleaning processes can help to minimize the amount of contamination.

In open-loop recycling, the material that is ground up is used in a lower-value application. A PET bottle, for example, turns into carpet fibers or plastic lumber. This allows bales of plastic with higher levels of contamination to find new uses in products that will last for many years. These types of materials cannot be economically recycled again, however, so once the carpet or lumber is discarded, it has to go to landfill.

Chemical recycling is another option. In this case, the polymers are broken down into individual monomers (the small molecules from which the polymers were originally made) which can provide feedstock to make new materials. Monomers recovered during chemical recycling substitute directly for the same monomers derived from fossil-fuel sources. The recovered monomers are chemically identical to conventional monomers, so they produce polymers of similar quality.

Nylon 6 is an example of a thermoplastic material that can be recycled many times using chemical recycling. This was the first material to be economically recycled using a chemical recycling process, beginning back in the 1990s. Aquafil, a global company based in Italy, makes a polymer called Econyl that's composed of entirely recycled nylon 6. Around half of the incoming material is scrap from nylon production and the other half is post-consumer waste. The post-consumer waste stream includes nylon fishing nets. Any nets brought in for recycling don't end up contributing to plastic trash in the oceans, providing an added benefit.

Companies are working on improving chemical recycling processes so that they can efficiently recycle a greater variety of plastic materials, including the most common thermoplastics used in disposable packaging. PET can be recycled by using solvents that reverse the polymerization reaction and return the material to individual monomers. The problem with this process is that it's very expensive, and it can be hard to remove pigments and additives.

Ioniqa Technologies in the Netherlands has developed an alternative process that uses magnetic catalysts to break down pigments. Because it removes all pigments, the company can process incoming material that is more varied. Mixed clear and colored PET bottles, along with textiles made from recycled PET, serve as feedstock to produce PET that is supposedly indistinguishable from virgin PET. Ioniqa has completed more than fifty test runs on its demonstration line in Rotterdam. As of mid-2018, Ioniqa was planning on opening a volume production factory in 2019.

Many of the bales of recyclables from the US and Europe have been getting shipped to China for mechanical or chemical recycling. These blocks of material have not needed to follow strict limits on contamination and often contained 10–20 percent contaminants, materials other than the specific material that was supposed to be in the bale. What happened to these bales? While concrete data are difficult to find, much of the material was incinerated.

In 2017, the Chinese government announced that it was changing the game. China was no longer going to serve as the world's trash compactor and would refuse to accept highly contaminated bales of materials for recycling. The US-based recycling industry views this turn of events as both a challenge and an opportunity. Without the option of sending bales overseas and shutting their eyes to the bales' eventual fate, companies need to improve their waste processing so more material is recycled locally.

European companies are stepping up to the challenge of creating high-quality recycled plastics. Startup Quality Circular Polymers (QCP) developed a cleaning technology that can remove more dirt and contaminants than conventional processes, producing a higher quality of recycled polyethylene and polypropylene that rivals the performance of virgin plastics. QCP shipped its first products in late 2015. Through a joint venture completed in 2018 between the plastics giant LyondellBasell and the waste management firm SUEZ, QCP's recycled plastics are now commercially available in Europe.

Chemical recycling hasn't been common because it's expensive. As the cost comes down, chemical recycling will provide a good way to create higher-value recycled plastics that have just the same quality as new virgin material and can be recycled over and over. Because of the efforts of multiple companies to expand chemical recycling processes, the prospect of truly circular plastic recycling is a real possibility. If all the common thermoplastics are recycled a sufficiently large number of times at a cost the market can bear, this will put a real dent in the accumulation of plastic waste.

The role of product design

Improving product design is another way to create a better recycling infrastructure. Although it has not historically been the norm, products can be designed with reuse and recycling in mind. For example, manufacturers can avoid the use of inks or glues that are difficult to clean off or impede recycling. Design changes are not easy since they require cooperation between many different companies involved in product design and manufacturing. In the case of swapping out inks or glues, limited availability of replacement materials that are compatible with commercial recycling stands in the way.

Reversible adhesives are another useful idea, one that appears especially promising for multilayer plastic pouches. The plastic packaging team of the American Chemistry Council makes bold claims about plastic pouch sustainability. Proponents, who have a vested economic interest, promote the benefits of these pouches: they protect food and prolong its shelf life without adding preservatives that consumers don't want to see in their food, thus reducing food waste.

Multilayer pouches come in two varieties: supported and unsupported. Unsupported pouches are those made entirely from thermoplastics. An exterior layer of polyethylene or polypropylene provides strength and heat resistance. A middle layer, consisting of a vinyl or nylon material, protects the contents from light and seals out undesirable gases or odors. The inner food-contact layer is made from LDPE or LLDPE and acts as a seal to keep food fresh. Additional layers of polyester- or acrylic-based adhesives are used to bond the main layers to one another. Supported pouches include layers of foil or paper in addition to thermoplastics.

The various materials bonded together in plastic pouches make the pouches nearly impossible to recycle. Multilayer pouches would be more recyclable if the individual layers could be easily separated from one another and sorted into their appropriate locations at a recycling facility. Easily dissolvable adhesives provide a possible solution. Ideally, pouches made with these adhesives would be water-soluble and would not require toxic solvents to dissolve the adhesives and separate the layers.

Product labeling also plays an important role in designing for recycling. Product designers unintentionally create recycling roadblocks when they only consider how a product will look on the store shelf. Full-color plastic sleeves on bottles attract attention, but they create sorting errors in systems that use optical recognition to sort different types of plastics. Paper labels pose another problem. They disintegrate when the plastic bottles are being washed and they also leave behind an adhesive residue that can contaminate the recycling stream. Possible solutions include replacing paper labels with plastic ones for plastic bottles or using water-soluble glues that can be washed off easily.

Forks with holes: separating compostable plastics

Product design can help with the sorting process at recycling facilities, in addition to its role in creating products that are recyclable. Compostable plastics like PLA should not be part of the recycling stream, but when consumers see a cup or fork that looks like plastic, their instinct is often to toss it into a recycling bin. People want to do the right thing, but if labeling isn't clear they can end up contaminating the recycling stream by mistake.

Manufacturers of compostable products are addressing this. Compostable flatware from World Centric has a cut-out in the handle in the shape of a leaf. This feature reminds consumers that this isn't an ordinary plastic fork or spoon. In addition, the hole can tell a sorting device that the object doesn't belong with the plastic recycling. The machine then sorts it into a separate bin headed for a composting facility. This concept, while helpful in theory, will only work if recycling facilities are equipped with machines that can distinguish between flatware with and without holes.

World Centric marks its PLA-based cold-drink cups as well. The cups have a green band that helps visually identify the product as being made from PLA so that optical sorting systems can separate it from plastic recycling streams. Optical sorting technology at a composting facility could recognize that a cup with a green band belongs with the compost, but composting facilities are not set up to incorporate optical sorting. Adding the technology would probably be far too expensive.

The compliance problem

Recycling initiatives face a challenge in convincing citizens to comply. When recycling and composting are inconvenient and confusing, people lack the incentive to do their part unless they have a personal conviction that overrides the challenge of complying.

A financial incentive to recycle always helps. Programs that involve container deposits are very effective in increasing recycling rates. In the state of Michigan, for example, stores collect ten cents for every container and return the fee when the consumer brings the container back. In 2016, the overall recycling rate in that state was 92 percent. Programs in the ten other states with deposit laws can't claim quite those results, but the states of California, Iowa, and Oregon all achieved relatively impressive recycling rates of more than 60 percent for plastic containers in 2017.

In the absence of financial incentives, the secret to getting consumers to recycle and compost regularly is to make the process easy and automatic. Labeling plays a role. Consider the frozen yogurt chain Yogurtland. When I walked over to throw away my cup and spoon at a Yogurtland store in 2016, I saw a clear plastic cylinder that exactly fit the yogurt cup and special compartments in which to toss the spoon and napkin. The implication was that these items would be automatically separated and sent for efficient recycling.

I asked the manager about the bins and whether the new process was corporate-wide. He said the setup did come from corporate, but each store chose whether to participate. I tried unsuccessfully to get data on how well the system is working. Either they don't know, or the answer is that the system isn't working so well. One problem with driving consumer compliance: my local store still had standard trash cans as well, so I'm sure some customers tossed their cups and spoons in the trash without noticing the new bins.

Fast-food or quick-serve restaurants provide a perfect opportunity to serve food with compostable plates, cups, spoons, and forks. Some are doing this this already, either because it ties into their corporate culture or because regulations are forcing their hand.

Taco Time in the Pacific Northwest uses nearly 100 percent compostable serving ware in its restaurants. The restaurants post clear signs indicating which items aren't compostable, such as juice boxes, and provide a small bin in which to toss these. In Molly Moon's, a popular chain of Seattle-area ice cream shops, every food-service item in the stores, from bowls to napkins, is compostable. The stores provide one bin for everything, with nothing going to landfill, making compliance simple.

Some quick-serve restaurants are still developing their recycling and composting processes. The seafood chain Ivar's, for example, serves its fish and chips in compostable containers, but the whole system is complicated. Paper trays, bowls, and cups (but not lids or straws) go in the compost bin, along with napkins and leftover food. But the small containers of ketchup and tartar sauce go in the trash can, along with straws. Some drink containers at Ivar's are recyclable but not compostable.

The result of this confusing system is that customers accidentally put stuff in the wrong bins, causing cross-contamination problems for the haulers and defeating the purpose of the separate containers. Also, figuring out what to put where and separating the napkins from the ketchup containers is such a pain that many people just toss everything into the garbage.

One of the reasons behind the confusion is variability in recycling laws and regulations from city to city. Inconsistent regulations can be especially challenging for companies that operate quick-serve restaurants in multiple cities and states.

Ivar's provides compostable serving containers in its restaurants in Seattle city limits because it has no choice. A 2010 law in the city prohibits food-service businesses from providing disposable containers for most items. For in-store dining, packaging must be compostable. Containers for to-go orders can be recyclable or compostable.

Beginning July 1, 2018, Seattle quick-serve restaurants like Ivar's also had to get rid of disposable plastic straws, when the city's latest ban went into effect. Compostable paper or plastic straws are acceptable, or restaurants can stop giving out straws entirely.

I ordered a beverage in Seattle before the straw ban, at a restaurant that had already switched to paper straws in preparation for the new law. Taking a sip brought me back in time to my 1970s childhood when stores sold boxes of paper straws decorated with colorful diagonal stripes. The taste of the paper slowly dissolving in my drink was nostalgic, but not in a good way. There's a good reason for plastic straws, though. Straws that dissolve—unless they are flavored edible straws designed for that purpose—do not make drinks taste better.

Rather than giving all customers paper straws, I think that food-service businesses shouldn't give out straws at all unless customers request them. Young children or those with a medical condition that makes drinking from a regular cup difficult can use a plastic straw. Or they can bring their own reusable straw or drinking container from home. Many years ago, I was at the Wild Animal Park in San Diego and requested a straw for my three-year-old son. A park employee informed me that they did not have any straws on the premises. Straws, she said, were a choking hazard for the animals. I don't recall how I dealt with the situation, but I'm sure my son managed somehow and didn't go thirsty.

On the surface, you might think that requiring all service ware and to-go containers be compostable and encouraging customers to deposit these items in compost bins is the best approach for sustainability. Unfortunately, it isn't that simple. As mentioned earlier, compostable packaging does not necessarily use fewer resources or have less environmental impact than other options. In addition to concerns about land and water use for producing PLA, some paper-based compostable containers are coated to minimize leakage, and these coatings often include toxic compounds. If a cardboard container is shiny on the inside, it's likely that the compost bin isn't the best place to toss it.

Unless more stringent standards are put in place to guide the design of compostable food-service ware, it's hard to know how to proceed. Meanwhile, encouraging clearer signage should at least limit cross-contamination of waste headed for recycling or composting.

◾ A look at plastic bags

Biodegradable bags can be especially troubling for recyclers. The EuPC, a trade association representing European Plastics Converters, completed a study in 2013 demonstrating the problems that biodegradable bags cause. They recycled virgin LDPE and several types of oxo-degradable plastics, which are plastics that degrade when exposed to air and sunlight. The oxo-degradable plastics were designed to be a more environmentally-friendly replacement for standard polyethylene bags, but they haven't lived up to that promise.

The EuPC study showed that recycled plastic containing even 2 percent oxo-degradable plastics was inferior to pure recycled LDPE in both appearance and mechanical strength. The researchers conducting the EuPC study concluded that conventional and biodegradable plastics need to be collected in separate recycling streams. Achieving this in practice requires clearer labeling and consumer education.

Oxo-degradable plastics are being phased out because of the problems they cause with plastic recycling, as well as the material's role in contributing to microplastic contamination in the oceans. Oxo-degradable is not the same as marine degradable, nor it is the same as compostable. Compostable bags pose a different set of concerns.

Polyethylene bags intended to transport organic produce home from the grocery store and compostable cornstarch-based bags are both often dyed green. The color green is associated with environmentally-friendly products but using the same color for two types of bags that shouldn't be commingled adds confusion. People don't want to take the time to read the fine print to figure out what type of benefit a green-colored product is promoting.

PCC (a natural foods grocery chain in the Seattle area) has stocked the hanging rods in its produce sections with several different types of colored plastic bags. During two visits a few weeks apart, I needed to read the fine print to figure out the purpose of the various colors.

During my first visit, the produce section sported bags colored a pale green. I grabbed one hanging above the apples when I saw that it was labeled "100 percent compostable and will biodegrade in 180 days." What better use of compostable bags than for storing food? I loaded the bag full of apples and took it home.

On my second visit, PCC had replaced the pale green bags with blue colored bags. I wondered whether the store was trying to stand out from the plethora of green-colored bags A closer look at the bags informed me that they are made from "100 percent Post Industrial Recycled Resin." I assume these are plastics that were used in some industrial process and have now been recycled into a form suitable for carrying fruits and vegetables.

The compostable bag had worked just fine, which is why when I finished buying my groceries I asked why the store no longer carried those bags. Apparently, not all customers found the bags as functional as I did. The clerk told me that people complained of the bags tearing, scattering produce all over the floor. Clearly, that would be a problem.

I expect that I handled the compostable bag more carefully than the average customer, knowing that it wouldn't be as strong as a conventional plastic bag. I compost at home and know that if I let the compost bin under my sink stay too many days without emptying it, the compostable liner starts to disintegrate. I have sometimes needed to double-bag my compost to get it safely to the yard waste bin without spilling half-rotten food all over the driveway.

For mass adoption, a greener solution needs to work as well as the conventional product it is replacing. I hope that Cedar Grove, the company whose name appeared on the compostable bag from PCC, creates a new version of the produce bag that is just a bit thicker. If it is durable enough to safely transport fruits and vegetables—even the heaviest ones—from the store to home, people will use it. Then maybe someday, all grocery stores, including the large chains, will carry only compostable bags in their produce sections.

Multiple ways to "recycle"

The umbrella of recycling incorporates several types of reuse: reusing materials from a discarded product to build new products, extending product lifespan, or creating energy from burning discarded materials.

Recycling of materials

The first type of reuse is the most common interpretation of the recycling concept. As discussed above, materials in discarded products are recycled by crushing and melting them to create materials for use in other products. Much of the reuse falls into the category of downcycling, where the products made from recycled materials require a lower grade of material and have less economic value.

Recycling of products

Using entire products or components more than once extends their lifespan. This benefit extends the life of a product by days, in the case of a plastic grocery bag reused as a trash bag, or years, in the case of a cell phone donated to an organization that provides free phones to victims of domestic violence.

The examples above involve the consumer's decision to reuse a product, but companies consider product lifespan when designing products or buying the supplies they need to run their businesses. Such decisions do not always tilt toward choosing products with a longer lifespan, of course, since longer product lifespan isn't necessarily the least expensive option, or the one that creates the most income for the company.

The concept of Life Cycle Assessment—evaluating a product through-out its life cycle, from raw materials sourcing through production, use, and disposal—incorporates the value of increasing product lifespan. Life Cycle Assessments are critical to understanding the most efficient ways to reduce waste. The results of these assessments are sometimes counterintuitive, lead-ing companies to make changes that they had not previously considered.

For example, consider crates used to ship fruits and vegetables. Plastic crates weigh 2 kg, compared to less than 1 kg for wooden or cardboard boxes, but the overall energy required to produce enough cardboard boxes to ship a million boxes of produce per year is more than twice that required when using wood or plastic boxes. Making cardboard requires more water and heat than making wood slats, but that isn't the main source of the difference. Cardboard crates don't last more than one or two shipments, whereas wood and plastic crates can be used dozens or even hundreds of times before they break.

Plastic crates are the most durable option because they are resistant to damage from moisture. If made from recycled plastic, the choice is by far the most environmentally friendly. The country of Sweden has streamlined the use of plastic shipping crates. All grocery stores in the country are required to receive goods in one of six standard sizes of reusable plastic crates, which are loaded onto reusable plastic pallets.

Recovering energy

As an alternative to recycling, recovered materials are sometimes burned to create energy. This type of reuse replaces other sources of energy such as envi-ronmentally damaging fossil fuels.

Burning materials for energy is not the same as replacing landfills with incinerators. The path to zero waste to landfill cannot involve merely incin-erating the waste. Incinerating mixed garbage releases toxic dust and creates ash. In addition to the environmental risks of incineration, incinerators that do not capture the energy from burning material are not a good choice finan-cially. They may also be a poor financial choice versus recycling: the city of Worcester, Massachusetts, introduced mandatory recycling in 1993. In doing so, they saved almost $100 million that would have been spent on a new incinerator to avoid overflowing landfills.

Waste-to-energy plants, as opposed to incinerators, create value by con-verting waste materials into useful energy. It is sometimes more cost-effec-tive to burn materials for energy than to separate streams of multiple recy-clable materials for use in low-value applications. If a recycling stream is contaminated with many different types of plastics, for example, it requires more energy to make a product from recycled plastic than to make one from new materials. In this case, burning the plastic, if done safely, makes more sense. Safely is the key word here. The toxic fumes released from burning must be captured to avoid endangering the health of workers and the local community.

Environmental regulations in many countries govern filtering of airborne toxins and disposal of any hazardous waste, which adds cost to the process without adding value. The common alternative used to be sending waste— either garbage or low-value mixed materials from recycling facilities—to countries without such regulations, where there is no requirement to capture the toxic dust.

China used to be among those countries, but with its new policies restricting imported garbage, waste handling companies face fewer options. Without an inexpensive way to dump excess plastic waste generated in the US and Europe, recycling facilities will need to adapt quickly to avoid being inundated with materials that they cannot sell locally or ship overseas. There will be a greater incentive to improve recycling in the country where the waste is generated or to send more material to waste-to-energy-plants.

Recycling processes, infrastructure, and practices need to improve in order to achieve the EU 2020 goal of zero waste to landfill. Incremental change in all these areas is happening, but that isn't enough. Fortunately, researchers and entrepreneurs are finding opportunities to innovate. Creative solutions to the problem of recycling especially challenging materials are on the horizon.

Worms that eat plastic

Polyethylene—the material in disposable grocery bags—is notoriously difficult to recycle. Efforts to help consumers separate plastic bags from the rest of their recyclables help. For example, grocery stores in some states serve as drop-off spots specifically for plastic bags. These bags can then be collected and sent to a recycling facility that has the ability to recycle them. But recycling remains a challenge, and better methods to process used polyethylene would be welcome.

Wax worms, the larvae of wax moths, may be the key that leads to a solution. In the wild, wax worms eat beeswax, much to the chagrin of beekeepers and anyone who cares about the importance of bees to our ecosystem. As Spanish scientist and amateur beekeeper Federica Bertocchini found out accidentally, the worms also consume polyethylene, the plastic in plastic gro-cery bags. Bertocchini, co-author of a study published in *Current Biology*, found wax worms in her beehive and captured them in a plastic bag. They ate through the plastic and ran amok.

Scientists believe that bacteria in the guts of wax worms may be respon-sible for their ability to consume polyethylene. Researchers are trying to fig-ure out whether the worms are eating through the plastic just to escape, or if they are using it as a food source. If the latter, that is much more promising, because it suggests that wax worms may have a continuing appetite for the material. If so, they may be able to eat constantly at a rate approaching that observed in the lab.

Lab tests show that one hundred wax worms can devour 92 milligrams of polyethylene in twelve hours. At this rate, it would take nearly half a million worms to consume one hundred plastic bags per day. Americans alone use more than 250 million bags per day. Breeding the billions of worms required to make a dent in our plastic trash problem comes with its own set of con-cerns. Any practical solution to the problem is therefore likely to lie in devel-oping enzymes resembling those that the wax worms produce.

What about composites?

The term "composite" means that the material is made from two or more dif-ferent materials fused together. Given the high amount of energy required to produce these materials (see the graph on page 110), recycling them is an especially good idea. Unfortunately, composite materials pose a unique chal-lenge when it comes to recycling. Recycling requires separating the various materials from each other so that they can be reused. It is not as simple as grinding and melting a product made from a single type of metal or plastic.

One material that comes to mind is Trex, a composite material used to build decks. It supposedly provides the best of both worlds, being a wood-like material that doesn't rot. Trex doesn't require the regular maintenance that wood decks demand to withstand exposure to rain and variations in tempera-ture through the seasons. What happens to Trex decks, however, when they are no longer needed?

Decking material made from polymers alone can probably be recycled, depending on the materials chosen. The planks of wooden decks will decom-pose once the nails and screws are removed, especially once any stains or paints have worn away. Trex, however, must be eventually destined for landfills. Still, composite decks last fifty or a hundred years, a factor that must be considered, and it is possible that new recycling methods will be available by then. A wood deck, if it lasted decades, would require a fresh coat of stain or paint applied every year or two. A thorough analysis needs to include production and disposal of the chemicals in these protective coatings.

Manufacturers making composite materials are investing research funds into evaluating potential methods to recycle these materials. High-performance composites hold enough economic value to provide an incentive to reuse them. Successful separation of the various components, if possible, allows each component of a composite material to find new uses in a completely different application than that of the original material.

Carbon-fiber composite materials, commonly used in sporting goods and aircraft, contain carbon in the form of graphite fibers. These are woven into a mat to form a carbon fabric. Epoxy is used to glue the fibers together. At this point, the composite fabric is called a "prepreg," meaning that it has been pre-impregnated with epoxy but is not ready for final use. Epoxy is a thermoset polymer (see the discussion of polymer types in Chapter 4), so the composite material needs to be cured at elevated temperature to attain its strength and durability.

Prepreg carbon-fiber sheets are relatively soft and flexible. They can easily be cut into any desired shape and layered to form a structure. Once cured, the resulting structures are strong, tough, and lightweight. This combination of properties makes them especially desirable for building sporting goods and aircraft. Carbon-fiber composites are also of interest for automotive applications and building wind turbine blades.

I can vouch for the value of carbon-fiber composites in sporting goods. I remember the first tennis racket I ever tried. It had been my father's and was made from wood. I was probably 4′4″ at the time and not very strong, and the racket was extremely heavy. It was hard for me to swing. My mother quickly realized it wasn't suitable for me to bring to beginning tennis lessons and bought me my own aluminum one. It was painted light blue and was light enough, especially since it was a small model built for children.

In the late 1980s, I again tried my hand at tennis and bought my own racket, an adult-sized model still made from aluminum. By the time my children were old enough to play tennis, carbon-fiber rackets had become available that were even lighter and easier to use. I still have my old aluminum racket—I engraved my name in the metal with a hand held engraving tool when I first bought it, so it has sentimental value—but I am acutely aware that it is not the best choice and I should play with a lighter racket to avoid muscle fatigue and swing more efficiently.

Back to recycling of carbon-fiber composites. There are two points during the life cycle of the material when it can be discarded. The first occurs during manufacturing, when cutting out pieces of prepreg sheets creates scrap waste. The second is at the end of life for objects made with carbon-fiber materials.

Carbon-fiber composite recycling methods do exist. Most methods use pyrolysis, in which cured material is heated to a sufficiently high temperature that it decomposes. The epoxy resin is burned off, and the carbon fiber remains. During pyrolysis, it is important to handle emissions appropriately so that no toxic fumes are released into the air. The companies doing this work understand that requirement.

The carbon fiber that remains after recycling cured composites is in the form of discontinuous threads, unlike the continuous woven threads in virgin composite material. The mechanical properties of sheets of material made from recycled carbon fibers are therefore compromised, which limits the applications for the recycled material. It can be reused to reinforce thermoplastics or thermosets, but the resulting product will not be as strong as a composite made with woven carbon fibers.

There are other options to effectively reuse recycled carbon fibers. 3-D printing poses one such possibility. Adding carbon-fiber reinforcement to thermoplastic filaments creates a stronger, tougher material for printing. This application doesn't require long, continuous threads of carbon fiber.

In the sporting goods industry, certain customers are able and willing to pay a premium for products made from recycled materials. Brands that want to associate themselves with environmentalism and sustainability will charge customers more for products that can boast recycled materials as one of their selling points. This provides a great opportunity for suppliers that can deliver recycled materials with sufficient mechanical strength. Startup Vartega is pursuing that path with its technology for recycling uncured carbon-fiber composite scrap.

INTERVIEW Andrew Maxey, Vartega

Andrew Maxey founded Vartega, a startup developing a new method for recycling of composite carbon-fiber materials, in 2014. His journey from engineer to entrepreneur involved a lucky accident.

In high school, Andrew worked in a bike shop. This was the late 1990s, when carbon-fiber bike frames were first becoming popular. Golf clubs and tennis rackets were starting to use carbon-fiber materials as well. One customer's misfortune turned out to be a career-changing experience for Andrew. This customer had driven home and into his garage with his expensive carbon-fiber bicycle loaded on the roof rack of his car. The bike was not salvageable, but the manufacturer graciously gave the customer a good deal on a replacement bike.

Meanwhile, Andrew took the cracked frame home and cut it up—he was intrigued by the material and wanted to understand it better. He wondered what it was. It didn't melt like metal, and it was so much lighter.

This experience led Andrew to pursue a college degree in mechanical engineering. Looking back, he wishes he had chosen materials science, but mechanical engineering served him well enough. Although Andrew's intention was to pursue a career in the sporting goods industry, that wasn't the way things turned out.

Andrew's path led him to textile processing and later to the oil and gas industry. But the memory of exploring the damaged carbon-fiber bicycle nagged at him. He wondered what happens to all that carbon-fiber material when it gets thrown away. Andrew figured he might be able to put his engineering experience to good use creating a better way to recycle the material.

Andrew conducted market research and discovered that dealing with scraps of uncured carbon-fiber composite presented the greatest opportunity. By his estimate, more than $600 million worth of carbon-fiber composite scraps are discarded into landfills every year. Andrew put together a team and founded Vartega to address two problems in the industry: the low quality of recycled carbon fiber and the high cost of recycling.

The aircraft industry creates vast quantities of prepreg scrap. Scrap rates are on the order of 30 percent of the volume of the starting materials. Even if it does send the scrap for recycling, an aircraft manufacturer like Boeing can't reuse it to build more planes. The strict reliability requirements the industry faces demand only the highest quality virgin material. This makes sense, because if cracks or other defects develop in an aircraft, the consequences can be dire. By contrast, no one is likely to die if their tennis racket breaks during a game.

Vartega developed a chemical process to separate the carbon fibers from the uncured epoxy, something that would be much more challenging if starting from fully cured material. Its process creates a material that is nearly as strong as virgin carbon composites. Vartega's first commercial processing facility opened in Denver, Colorado, in 2018. Andrew's long-term vision places carbon fiber recycling facilities throughout the world located near waste-stream sources. A facility in the Pacific Northwest would collect prepreg from aircraft manufacturing, whereas one in the Midwest would focus on scrap from the automotive industry.

Although it's too early to know whether Andrew's vision will pan out, Vartega is a company worth watching.

Packaging milk and soap

Earlier in this chapter, I mentioned replacing single-use items with reusable versions as a good strategy for reducing waste. This is possible in practice, but it requires undoing decades of ingrained habits. Reusable packaging is no longer common in products sold directly to consumers, at least in urban regions of the developed world. Decades ago, people used to get their food more directly from the farm.

It now seems quaint thinking of a time when milk was delivered daily in glass bottles to the door. The milkman (I suspect it was always a man in those days) would pick up the empty bottles to be cleaned and refilled. Milk delivery services have resurfaced. Smith Brothers Farms delivers dairy products and other foods to the doorstep in Seattle-area neighborhoods, for example, but the milk comes in standard cartons.

But I have purchased milk in glass bottles recently. The first time was in 2004, when I was traveling through rural Missouri and stopped by a farm that offered free tastings and milk to sell. It was the most delicious milk ever, probably because it was both fresh and stored in glass. A decade later, I found Strauss Milk at Whole Foods stores in California, in glass bottles. The store charged a deposit on the bottles, which we got back when we returned the bottles to the store. Strauss, the manufacturer, was responsible for cleaning and refilling the bottles. Other companies also provide dairy products in glass containers and handle exchanges at the stores that carry their products.

Stores in communities with many environmentally-oriented residents have tried other approaches, such as having customers refill reusable containers that they bring from home with bulk goods like laundry detergent. Replenish, based in Los Angeles, sells reusable containers along with refill pods of active ingredients in concentrated form. Consumers add water and mix up a new batch of product. The company intends the containers to be reused around thirty times.

It's hard to know whether the desire to use less packaging will win out over the desire for the convenience of disposable packaging. Without widespread adoption of the reuse model, it won't do a lot of good. Replenish announced a partnership with Walmart in 2015, with Walmart stores using Replenish spray bottles and refill pods in a line of cleaning and personal care products. A search on the Walmart website in 2018, however, yielded no such products. They must not have sold well.

As with bans on plastic bags, sometimes regulations are what it takes to spur behavior changes and investment in different ways of doing things. For example, a 2014 law in San Francisco outlawing the sale of single-use water bottles on city property convinced the city to install more drinking fountains and reusable bottle refill stations.

The ideal plastic

The ideal plastic material of the future would solve all the problems with conventional plastics. It would be strong, durable, formable, and possess all the desirable properties of the best-performing plastic materials in common use today. It would be easily recyclable using mechanical or chemical recycling processes, enabling it to be recycled many times while maintaining the properties of the virgin material. This hypothetical ideal plastic would be made from renewable resources and produced in a manner that would not negatively impact growth of food crops.

The ideal plastic would be bio-benign, causing no harm to the oceans or sea creatures if accidentally released into waterways. Creating a bio-benign plastic that degrades in marine environments is especially challenging. Such a material must disintegrate rapidly into small fragments, less than 2 mm in size. The small size reduces the risk of entanglement or strangulation of marine animals, but that feature alone is not sufficient. These plastic materials would have to be nontoxic, containing no additives that would endanger marine life in case of ingestion.

Methods of producing the ideal plastic would need to consider multiple potential issues, including energy use, water use, human health risks, and the effect on lakes and oceans. Not only should the end product be nontoxic and bio-benign, no step in its production should pose a health risk and emissions should be kept as low as possible.

This hypothetical ideal plastic material remains elusive and may never come to fruition. Despite the challenge involved, scientists and engineers should work to develop products that move toward the ideal plastic. At the same time, society should make efforts to reduce the use of disposable plastic packaging regardless of how it is made or the sources of the raw materials.

The best realistic solution is to have a suite of plastics available for applications where substituting a completely different material creates more problems than it solves. Plastics such as polyethylene and polypropylene should be made without the use of fossil fuels, either through recycling the existing mountains of plastic trash or by replacing these conventional plastics with biobased plastics.

The methods of producing biobased plastics matter—agriculture using large quantities of water and pesticides can have a more negative environmental and human health impact than producing plastics from fossil-fuel feedstocks. The Oregon Department of Environmental Quality (DEQ) evaluated results from scientific studies and concluded that just because a plastic is biobased doesn't mean that it is a better choice from a safety and environmental standpoint. But biobased plastics produced using sustainable feedstocks and nontoxic production methods are a good alternative to conventional plastics.

Industrially compostable plastics fulfill an important role in reducing waste, but they are not suitable for all applications, and research from the Oregon DEQ (see Chapter 4) also exposed concerns about compostable materials and composting food-service ware. Compostable plastics can still be improved upon to be stronger during use while degrading faster under the right conditions of temperature and humidity.

Tossing mountains of used packaging materials into recycling bins and assuming that they will magically be turned into valuable new products is naive. Still, infrastructure for recycling is moving in the right direction. New technologies for sorting and processing waste are encouraging. How much difference will these changes make? It's hard to say. Ingrained habits are hard to break. The hard truth is that businesses will not shift their practices unless it saves them money or allows them to break even while improving their reputations with customers. Very few individuals will change their practices unless doing so is easy and convenient. But if we continue to educate ourselves and those around us about effective recycling practices, progress will occur.

CHAPTER 7

Tackling the E-waste Monster

"Every time you buy a new electronic device, you're
likely funding the conflict mineral industry."
—Peter Holgate, Ronin8

"It's ridiculous that we still extract metals that
are abundantly available above ground."
—Joost de Kluijver, Closing the Loop

Mountains of cell phones

"Mom, how old were you when you got your first cell phone?"

I did a quick mental calculation. "Thirty-three."

My son seemed momentarily astounded, as though he had forgotten that cell phones have not been around forever. To someone born in the late 1990s, however, it may seem that way. Around 1.5 billion cell phones are produced every year. There is something wrong with a world where more people own cell phones than have access to running water. That statistic reminds me that we, as a global community, need to work harder to provide more people with safe running water, and also that the production of consumer electronics contributes to the toxic environments in which many people in the world live.

Any effort to shift away from the disposable society will face tremendous resistance. Electronic products are designed with frequent replacement in mind. Marketing campaigns are designed to convince consumers that they must have the latest and greatest version. Planned obsolescence is not limited to consumer electronics, though that is the market where the practice causes the most unintended harm.

Planned obsolescence does drive innovation—one of the positive effects that manufacturers are touting—but also creates a great deal of waste. An obscenely high number of cell phones are discarded every year, not because they no longer work, but because people buy newer models to replace them.

Cell phones contribute a significant portion of the growing electronic waste (e-waste) problem because of the vast number produced and market forces telling consumers that their phones need to be replaced every year or two. In 2009, an estimated 130 million cell phones were discarded in the US alone, and this quantity has only grown since.

These discarded cell phones contain a wealth of materials that could potentially be reused. These materials include metals, semiconductors, glass, plastics, and ceramics. How much valuable material do 130 million cell phones hide? Quantities range from 4 tonnes of gold to 9,000 tonnes of plastics. One tonne, also known as a metric ton, equals 1,000 kilograms or about 2,200 pounds.

Cell phone manufacturing requires up to two dozen different metals. Some, such as aluminum and copper, are used in significant quantities in a single phone. Others are present as trace elements in alloys or as minute additions to the glass or plastic of the phone's screen and casing. Gold is the most valuable

Metric tons of material in 130 million cell phones

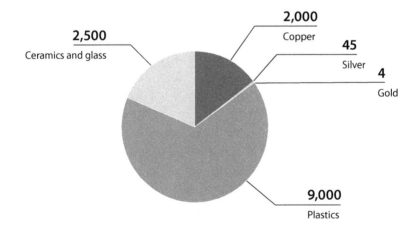

Data from Vaclav Smil, *Making the Modern World*

E-waste regulation timeline

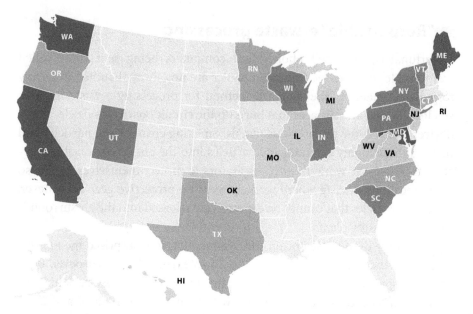

Electronics Recycling Coordination Clearinghouse,
www.ecycleclearinghouse.org

- 2003–2006: CA, MD, ME, WA
- 2007: CT, MN, NC, OR, TX
- 2008: HI, IL, NJ, MI, MO, OK, RI, VA, WV
- 2009–2011: IN, NY, PA, SC, UT, VT, WI

metal inside phones, and the most likely to be recovered when phones are recycled, but all metals in the phone have economic value.

Among the many materials in cell phones are small quantities of toxic metals such as lead, cadmium, and mercury. As we ship our e-waste to China and other countries where environmental regulations aren't as stringent as they are in North America and Europe, we are subjecting workers to toxins and also leaching those toxins into their communities' water supplies.

What should we do about the e-waste problem? Stemming the flow of e-waste is not possible in the current consumer environment. The companies that produce electronics benefit from encouraging increased adoption worldwide, and their customers in regions with limited resources benefit as well from access to global information. I would argue for replacing electronic devices less frequently, but even that will do little to fix the problem. We, as a global society, need to process our e-waste in a less toxic manner.

"Responsible" e-waste processing

Unfortunately, even cell phones and computers being sent to so-called "responsible" e-waste recycling companies are not always handled in a truly responsible manner. The standard method for processing e-waste involves smelters, which are furnaces that burn up the circuit boards inside electronic devices and recover the precious metals. Smelting creates toxic particles and releases these highly carcinogenic particles into the air. At responsible recycling facilities, the workers wear respirators to protect themselves, unlike so many locations in Asia where workers wear no protective gear whatsoever. Still, tiny particles that cannot be captured are released into the air surrounding the processing plants.

I have only lived in California and Washington, so it surprised me to learn that half of the states in the US have no e-waste regulations whatsoever. But I am not surprised that California was the first to enact such a law, back in 2003. Washington and Oregon followed suit with their versions in 2006 and 2007, respectively, to cover the entire West Coast. There are no federal rules regarding e-waste, and it is highly unlikely that the current administration will enact any.

Having state laws, however, is no guarantee that e-waste will be recycled properly. For example, breaking news in September 2016 told the story of Total Reclaim, a Washington state "responsible" recycler that was illegally dumping e-waste overseas rather than processing it locally, as its certification as a green recycler required. The state fined Total Reclaim, Washington's largest recycler, almost half a million dollars. Oregon, a state in which Total Reclaim also operated, followed suit in 2017 by imposing a fine and banning the company from collecting e-waste.

This story is just another example of consumers being duped, thinking we were doing the right thing by bringing our old electronics to an e-waste facility. Since the story aired, Total Reclaim claims to have taken multiple steps to improve its recycling processes and try to regain the public's trust as an "environmentally responsible recycler."

Smokey Peck, the president of Interwest Paper whose interview appeared in the previous chapter, told the story of Stone Castle, an e-waste recycler that was facing fines from the EPA and potential jail time for its executives. The owner had fled the area, leaving behind mountains of e-waste at several facilities that "magically" kept catching fire.

Putting our heads in the sand is the easy way out. We drop our e-waste off at what looks like a legitimate recycling location and assume it will be dealt with properly. In the best case, the e-waste will be processed locally, at facilities where the workers wear suitable protection from lead, cadmium, and the toxic dust and fumes created by grinding and incinerating the circuit boards from old cell phones and computers.

In the worst case, e-waste will be shipped to facilities where workers are subjected to dangerous conditions every day. In countries without strict labor laws, children work dismantling computers and tossing the circuit boards into smelters. In many e-waste recycling facilities, both in North America and abroad, prisoners work essentially as slave labor.

Until electronics companies demand better e-waste recycling or regulations require it, truly responsible e-waste handling remains elusive. The best way to ensure that a so-called responsible e-waste recycler is doing what it says is to physically go into a plant and audit the recycling company's practices.

Companies that collect used electronic devices from customers can choose an e-waste recycling facility that calls itself responsible and hope for the best, or look deeper to find the facility most likely to process the e-waste safely. They have other options as well: the landfill or incineration.

Sending e-waste to a landfill is, surprisingly, a more responsible choice than shipping it to recyclers overseas. Laura Turbini at Georgia Tech researched landfill management and concluded that no measurable amount of lead was leaching into soils from electronics discarded into landfills. From the perspective of protecting people from lead poisoning, therefore, dumping e-waste into landfills is a much better option than sending it to unregulated disassembly and incineration facilities overseas. While Turbini's research focused on lead, presumably the results for cadmium and mercury would be similar.

Using an arc plasma smelter is another option that represents a step up from landfilling. Blue Oak Resources in Arkansas is one company promoting this technology. The idea is that by burning e-waste at extremely high temperatures—around 1,600 degrees—it is possible to burn off the toxic volatile compounds and somehow capture the fumes. Burning the waste avoids contaminating landfills with lead or other toxins.

Sound waves instead of heat

Another alternative to smelting for e-waste processing lies on the horizon. Ronin8, based in Vancouver, British Columbia, has pioneered an innovative, nontoxic approach to processing e-waste.

Before printed circuit boards enter a smelter, machines mechanically shred them. Shredding creates toxic dust and wastes a certain fraction of the material, including valuable gold. Ronin8 figured out a way to avoid creating dust in the first place.

The Ronin8 process starts with shredding circuit boards, but it does so under water. The water is then squeezed through multiple filters, removing finer and finer particles, until it is sufficiently clean and gets fed back into the system for the next batch of material. Because the cutting and separating occur under water, the process generates no dust. This means not only avoiding toxic fumes but reclaiming nearly all the materials in the circuit board.

The number 8 in Ronin8's name is not accidental. The shape of the 8 represents a closed-loop, circular economy, where everything is recycled continuously. The filtered water goes around and around.

The key step in Ronin8's metal recovery process uses a low-frequency, high-amplitude sonic generator to generate sound waves. The machine contains a giant bar of steel driven by electromagnets. When the steel vibrates at its resonant frequency, it acts like a massive tuning fork and becomes a very efficient energy generator. The resulting energy is concentrated in water-filled chambers attached to either side of the steel bar that contain a slurry made from the shredded circuit boards.

The trick lies in how different elements in the slurry respond to the sound waves. Materials with higher density (weight per unit of volume) experience greater vibrations than do lighter materials. Polymers have nearly the same density as water, whereas metals are much denser. Since the sonic energy has a disproportionate effect on the metals, it shakes them loose from the rest of the mixture. The system, therefore, creates two waste streams: one of plastic and one of metal.

The sonic generator doesn't handle every part of a cell phone, but it comes close. Ronin8 removes the lithium-ion batteries from phones before shredding them and works with a separate supplier to recycle the cover glass. The Ronin8 process recovers a metal concentrate containing up to twenty-four different metals. In contrast, most smelters and refineries recover only the most valuable metals—gold, silver, copper, and a few others. Only 5 percent of the rare earth metals are recovered in standard smelting processes.

The metals extracted from the sonic generator come out as tiny slivers, ready to resell to metal refineries. The refineries then melt and refine the alloys to separate the metals they need.

Ronin8 didn't invent the sonic generator technology. It comes from Placer Dome, a mining company that Barrick Gold Corporation acquired in 2006.

Barrick's plan for the sonic generator was to use it to extract gold from tailings, the leftover low-grade ore languishing in heaps at mining sites. Traditional mining can economically extract gold from high-grade ore, but about 10 percent of the ore doesn't contain sufficient quantities of gold to be worth processing. Mines keep these tailings for an undefined time in the future when technology will have presumably advanced sufficiently to allow the gold to be efficiently extracted.

Sonic generators can do more than extract precious metals. Back in 2004, a now-defunct company called Sonic Environmental Solutions used Annacis Island as a proving ground for Placer Dome's sonic generator technology. The idea was to extract toxic polychlorinated biphenyl (PCB) compounds from the soil. Sonic Environmental Solutions posed its concept as an alternative to shipping contaminated soil to incinerator facilities. Instead of incinerating the soil at high temperatures, they load the soil into the sonic generator. The vibrations separate the toxins, and a solvent helps turn the chlorine component of the biphenyls into sodium chloride ($NaCl$), better known as table salt.

Is it a coincidence that the acronym for polychlorinated biphenyls, PCB, also stands for printed circuit boards? With my background in the semiconductor packaging industry, the first thing that comes to my mind when I hear "PCB" is "printed circuit board."

In the context of Annacis Island, however, PCB obviously means polychlorinated biphenyls. These compounds were probably remnants of pre-1977 light fixtures, which contained the carcinogenic compounds before they were banned from consumer products. Sonic generators can handle both types of PCBs, either neutralizing toxic chemicals or recovering valuable metals. Ronin8 CEO Peter Holgate is convinced that the second option represents the future of e-waste processing.

INTERVIEW   Peter Holgate, Ronin8

Peter Holgate conveys an air of confidence without seeming arrogant. His desire to achieve something "consequential" with his third startup drove him to found Ronin8. I interviewed Peter in his office in downtown Vancouver, British Columbia.

Peter inherited a legacy of mining, having grown up in South Africa as the descendant of two grandfathers who had made their careers in the mining industry. One grandfather had been the general manager of Simmer and Jack Mines in Johannesburg, the largest gold mine in the world at the time.

By the time Peter was an adult, he was well aware of the benefits and consequences of digging up minerals from the Earth. As a child, however, he had been blissfully ignorant. He tells tales of sliding down sandy hillsides in Johannesburg that were, unbeknownst to Peter and his friends, laced with cyanide. The wonderfully powdery sand also made a great base for laying bricks in gardens. The local families had no idea the stuff was toxic.

Peter's journey into the world of e-waste begins with his mother, a larger-than-life woman who inspired him while also instilling a sense of fear that he might not live up to her almost impossibly high expectations. In 2013, shortly after his mother's death, Peter received a letter from her in the mail. One paragraph is seared into his memory.

"I just had lunch with Michael Musk. Michael tells me that Elon has launched a rocket ship into space and successfully landed it on a platform in the Pacific Ocean. How's your career coming along? Love, Mom." Apparently, Peter's mom had connections. She and Michael, Elon's uncle, had grown up in the same community.

Peter's career thus far hadn't been too shabby. He had built up and sold two businesses over the previous twenty years and was trying to figure out what he wanted to do next. To honor his mother's memory, he wanted to do something meaningful that would gift his children a lasting legacy. After learning that e-waste is the fastest growing waste stream in the world and watching the documentary *Digital Dumping Ground*, Peter decided to do something about e-waste.

He started with the idea of tackling urban mining and improving it but then considered the circular economy. Why continue to mine more metals when we can recover those already mined over the past century? The technology of smelting hadn't changed in 200 years. Peter and his colleagues decided that an alternative to smelting was necessary.

Ronin8 is making advances toward commercializing its technology. The company's efforts start with its 20,000-square-foot facility in Richmond, British Columbia, near Vancouver. Peter understands that the large electronics companies such as Apple, Dell, and Intel don't want to switch processes unless they are convinced that the new process can scale to high volume. This is the standard chicken-and-egg scenario any time an entrenched industry is being wooed by an upstart process that proposes something completely different from business as usual.

The Richmond facility, funded by the $10 million in venture capital that Ronin8 has attracted, is their answer to potential objections and wariness. It is a prototype plant loaded with full-scale equipment that can process up to 1 or 2 tons of material per day. To scale up further, they will need to increase the speed of materials handling and buy more sonic generators.

Peter, now the former CEO of the company, had a vision that featured Ronin8 e-waste processing plants located throughout the world—anywhere where e-waste is discarded. Each plant could be up and running in three months and would be able to process 5,000 tons of material per year. The goal is $30 million in revenue per plant. The first step toward that vision is to cover North America, adding centers in the US and Mexico.

In locations from Pittsburgh to Hong Kong, the plan would place new plants conveniently close to existing smelters to provide a more environmentally-friendly alternative to smelting. And by building a plant in the Pacific Northwest, where no nearby smelter exists, Ronin8 aims to convince decision-makers in the region that they don't need to install a smelter.

Listening to Peter, his vision sounds feasible. I believe that it does have the potential to change the world in a substantial, consequential way. Will it happen within two years? That sounds optimistic. But I expect that Ronin8 will succeed.

Too few people truly want to make a positive difference in the world and are willing to do the due diligence necessary to make it happen, but Peter seems genuinely invested in doing the right thing. He is willing to turn down business opportunities if potential vendors or customers don't share his values, and he won't stand for greenwashing. Yes, Peter is ambitious, and yes, he wants to create a profitable venture, but he hasn't let those desires get in his way of being a responsible corporate citizen.

What about the batteries?

Recovering valuable metals like gold is standard practice in e-waste processing. Metals that command lower prices per ounce haven't historically been recovered because the cost of extracting them from e-waste is too high given their resale value. I expect that new techniques from companies like Ronin8 will change the equation.

Meanwhile, some relatively low-cost metals are facing potential shortages as demand escalates. Shortages will drive up metal prices and motivate greater recovery and recycling efforts. Lithium, a crucial component of batteries, is one of these metals.

Lithium-ion batteries are removed before consumer electronics are processed at e-waste recycling facilities and recycled independently. Battery recycling comes with a set of unique challenges. At present, recycling lithium does not make sense economically. The lithium is much less valuable than the cobalt or nickel inside lithium-ion batteries, and it is present in such small quantities that the cost of recycled lithium is much greater than that of virgin lithium. Today's lithium battery recycling efforts are directed at keeping batteries out of landfills and recovering the more valuable cobalt and copper inside them to resell.

In the future, however, soaring lithium prices could make recycling the metal worthwhile. Lithium prices tripled from 2001 to 2011, reaching $6,000 per ton. And by mid-2017, lithium was selling for $20,000 per ton in China. Increasing demand for lithium-ion batteries for both consumer electronics and electric vehicles, combined with limited resources concentrated in South America, are expected to keep prices on the rise.

Lithium-ion battery recycling is being done, just not with the recovery of lithium as the primary goal. Umicore has been providing lithium-ion battery recycling services since 2006 and claims to have a unique recycling process. The company also recycles lithium polymer and nickel metal hydride batteries.

Umicore's "pyro-metallurgical treatment" sounds like a fancy way to say that it incinerates the batteries in a high-temperature furnace. But there is more to it than that. The company claims to use the energy present in the batteries to power the process, reducing total energy consumption. Following incineration, Umicore refines the alloy using a "hydro-metallurgical process," which I suppose involves water.

Umicore's recycling process reclaims cathode materials—cobalt, nickel, and copper—to be used to produce new batteries. The company has a large facility, with the capacity to handle 7,000 metric tons of materials per year. That's the equivalent of 250 million phone batteries or 35,000 electric vehicle batteries.

Li-Cycle Corporation, a startup in Ontario, Canada, is tackling lithium recycling directly. It claims to have created a process to profitably recycle lithium from lithium-ion batteries. Its process also recovers cobalt and copper. Li-Cycle boasts low energy consumption, low carbon emissions, and zero waste to landfill, which sounds impressive compared to existing industry-leading battery recycling processes.

The Li-Cycle website is purposely vague about the details, presumably to keep a lid on their proprietary process. In response to a customer question about how they recover the metals efficiently, the company answered, "We achieve recovery through our validated and scalable recycling technology."

The conflict mineral problem

Mining has a second dark side, beyond the damage to the Earth. Many of the minerals that society relies on are found in war-torn regions, where working conditions are extremely unsafe. As a result, slavery is still happening today in Africa. People are being forced at gunpoint to dig up minerals out of the ground.

Minerals mined under extremely unsafe working conditions are known as conflict minerals, and cell phones are full of them. The tantalum used in capacitors and resistors, tungsten filaments, tin in solder, and gold in circuit board connections are all conflict minerals. They are mined in Angola, Rwanda, and the Congo. As of 2017, the cobalt in batteries wasn't yet on the conflict mineral list, but was heading that way.

The situation is not completely straightforward. There are mines in the world where industry-leading safety practices are common and where worker abuses are not part of the problem. But the global supply chain is complex, meaning that many different companies are involved in the path from extracting a metal ore from the Earth to selling a finished cell phone. Cell phone manufacturers often do not know the sources of the metals in their devices. So long as manufacturers can get the materials they need, at a cost they can afford, they don't necessarily dig deeper.

There are hints that things may be changing. Apple made an audacious announcement in 2017, publicly stating a goal to eliminate mined rare earth elements from its iPhones. Stating such a goal, without a concrete plan in place to achieve it, was unheard of from the usually secretive Apple.

It is not clear at this time how Apple will manage to remove mined metals from its phones, especially given the relatively short timeline of product development. Apple has set up a system where consumers expect a new phone every couple of years. The technology to produce rare earth metals without mining is not ready to handle the huge volume of materials that a company like Apple requires.

Any solution that reduces the amount of mining required automatically addresses conflict minerals, so Apple's goal is laudable. Urban mining, where items like discarded cell phones are removed from landfills and sent to e-waste recycling facilities, is going to be the route that enables such a shift. The trick is to improve the e-waste infrastructure and create economies of scale so that all the metals needed to make the next generation of electronics can be recovered at a reasonable cost.

INTERVIEW Joost de Kluijver, Closing the Loop

Joost de Kluijver believes that cell phones are vital for communication, entrepreneurship, and sometimes even for human rights. Digital access has a positive impact on several of the United Nations' Sustainable Development Goals, especially in emerging markets. But Joost became concerned—rightly so—about what was happening to cell phones at the end of life. In response, he founded Closing the Loop as a non-governmental organization (NGO) in 2012, with the ambition of collecting scrap phones in emerging markets. He discovered instead that there was a financial opportunity related to old phones and reorganized the NGO into a social enterprise organization in 2014. Closing the Loop is based in Amsterdam, The Netherlands.

Closing the Loop participates in three primary endeavors:

1. Running a "One for One" offset program, in which a corporate customer in Europe buys phones for their employees and Closing the Loop collects scrap phones in Africa on behalf of the customer, who pays a fee for the service and can claim the new phones are "material neutral."

2. Collecting cell phones from countries in Africa—where there are no convenient recycling facilities and phones typically end up in landfills—and shipping them to responsible recyclers in Europe.

3. Collecting used phones that still work and giving them a second life in emerging markets, using a closed-loop process: for each phone Closing the Loop ships to Africa, it collects one scrap phone locally and ensures that it gets recycled.

The offset program is attractive to companies wanting to improve their corporate image while funding Closing the Loop's collection efforts. The concept is similar to carbon offsets, where companies pay to balance their carbon dioxide emissions with projects that, for example, plant trees to sequester carbon dioxide. It seems like a bit of a shell game. Joost admits that "it's based on a bit of a medieval concept, like paying the church some money and your sins are somehow relieved." Joost still believes, however, that those who pollute should pay for polluting. Offset programs can be a good first step toward a more circular model.

Materials are much more tangible than carbon emissions, and Closing the Loop is bringing materials back into production cycles that would otherwise end up in landfills. The principle is fairly straightforward. For every used phone recovered for recycling, less gold needs to be extracted from mining to make a new phone.

Joost pointed out that steps that people are willing to take now, even if limited in scope, are more effective than more ambitious concepts that appear too expensive or will require efforts that people aren't willing to make.

The next step after collecting phones is properly recycling them. Joost says that there are probably five factories in the world—Umicore in Belgium is one—that can recycle e-waste reasonably safely and efficiently. He recognizes that e-waste processing still uses energy and creates pollution, but he takes comfort in the fact that it's much better than mining from an environmental standpoint.

Closing the Loop relies on partners to support its vision. One of those is T-Mobile Netherlands, which promotes the concept that cell phones should never end up as waste and encourages its customers to repair and upgrade their phones rather than discard them after a year or two.

Joost would like his company to be seen as being a metals supplier and not only a waste collector. He would love to collaborate with Apple to help them achieve their goal of making phones using no newly mined metals.

Joost hopes that Closing the Loop will demonstrate that circular business models are possible and bring both environmental and financial benefit to companies. NGOs need to move past thinking of large companies as the bad guys and work with them to create better business models that create a positive impact on society. The first steps may be pragmatic and imperfect, but such efforts are necessary in the path toward a more circular economy.

Responsible mining?

The website of Barrick Gold Corporation states, "Our vision is the generation of wealth through responsible mining." Surely that is better than conducting irresponsible mining to make a profit regardless of the company's impact on workers and the surrounding communities, but Barrick's vision is necessarily myopic. Mining companies need to continue mining if they want to stay in business.

Ideally, electronics manufacturers will become vocal advocates of the circular economy. They will migrate toward corporate policies that support best practices for choosing the materials that come into their factories, how they process these materials, and the eventual fate of the products they produce. They will encourage their customers to return electronic devices and consumables like ink cartridges for recycling.

A shift toward different models of producing electronics will help reduce the need for mining as well. Fairphone, a niche player in the electronics industry, promotes the idea that cell phones should be modular, allowing customers to replace and upgrade individual components instead of discarding a phone for a new model. As of 2018, Fairphone's modular cell phones are only available on a small scale in Europe, limiting the company's potential impact. Modular cell phones can only become mainstream if companies like Fairphone partner with the major manufacturers such as Apple and Samsung. Small players can't compete head-to-head with the giants, but maybe a collaboration could offer true choice to consumers.

Some prominent companies are taking action or making public statements that demonstrate their concern about toxic manufacturing or disposal of their products. Apple hasn't committed to any specific deadline regarding their goal of eliminating mined metals, but I'm sure Ronin8 would also be delighted to work with Apple to accelerate the transition. HP is another company making strides toward better e-waste management with its comprehensive inkjet cartridge recycling program.

The shift in attitude is happening because of both economic and social pressure. Reclaiming metals from electronics creates a new stream of materials that cost less than metals mined from the Earth. In affluent countries, consumers are more likely to want to buy from companies that are trying to minimize the negative environmental impact of their products.

Consumer electronics are here to stay, but it is possible to reduce the environmental hazards associated with their production. Improved e-waste recycling is one method. Changing the way products are manufactured represents another avenue. Keep reading to see how printing is revolutionizing the manufacturing of everything from cell phones to bridges.

CHAPTER 8

Manufacturing and Processing Methods

"We've shipped billions of inkjet cartridges with closed-loop recycled plastic in them. The careful control of the input material is what allows us to use it in a highly engineered application."

—Judy Glazer, HP

▇ The big picture

Parts I and II of this book talked about manufacturing in the context of producing both products—gasoline, cell phones, airplanes—and the chemicals and materials needed to make these products. I emphasized the importance of reducing the use of toxic substances in all the steps of manufacturing, starting with extracting minerals from the Earth through building end products with metals and plastics.

This chapter focuses on the latter stage—starting with a concept for a product and having chosen the design and the materials from which to build it, what options are available for constructing the final product? Do certain options suggest changes in the design or materials?

I recommend considering manufacturing options in light of the four system conditions, introduced in Chapter 2. These conditions lay out the responsibility of product manufacturers to consider ways to minimize the quantity of material extracted from the Earth, the production of toxic substances, the destruction of natural resources, and the exposure of workers to unsafe working conditions.

With the four system conditions in mind, ask specific questions when looking at various manufacturing methods. How do the different options compare when considering worker exposure to toxins during manufacturing? Do any toxins from the manufacturing process remain in the end product, creating a risk for customers or those handling product disposal at the end of its life cycle?

What about the waste created during manufacturing? How can our society move toward a more circular economy? As we've seen already, choices in design and materials affect the volume of waste created, and there are opportunities for recycling at various points along the way. Manufacturing methods also play a role.

Additive versus subtractive manufacturing

Manufacturing processes can be either additive, in which a product is built up by adding successive layers of material, or subtractive, in which a product is formed by starting with a block or layer of material and removing excess material to create the desired shape.

Traditional manufacturing of parts that go into final products relies on subtractive processes. The excess material that doesn't end up in the final product becomes waste. The waste can often be recycled. Companies that machine parts out of metal will ideally collect scraps and shavings and send them for refining into recycled metal. As we've seen in the previous chapters, this concept works much better for metals than for plastics.

Manufacturing of plastic parts often requires methods other than machining. Options include injection molding and extruding.

Injection molding involves injecting liquid thermoplastics into cold metal molds so that the plastic quickly solidifies into the desired shape. The process is inexpensive and efficient, but it doesn't work well for complex shapes. Injection-molded parts need additional grinding to remove burrs, and sometimes machining to add more intricate design features.

Extruding forces thermoplastics through holes in a die, somewhat like making homemade pasta or using a play-dough press. It's a low-cost way to make rods or sheets, which are then machined into final parts as needed.

Additive manufacturing, where three-dimensional (3-D) parts are deposited layer by layer in a precise pattern, comes with several benefits when compared to traditional subtractive methods:

- Designers can change the physical shape of an object by editing a software file.

- Material waste is minimal.
- There is no need to melt large quantities of material at once, saving the energy needed for high-temperature ovens.

Additive manufacturing should theoretically result in less waste and less use of toxic chemicals, but that isn't always true in every case. Companies can't necessarily say truthfully that their product is more environmentally friendly than a competitor's product just because they build it with additive manufacturing. Multiple factors affect the overall picture including materials, product volume, and manufacturing strategy.

The materials used and their source. Printing a 3-D shape from virgin materials is more wasteful and energy-intensive than machining one out of recycled materials.

The number and variety of products produced. Additive manufacturing is best suited to creating unique designs or a small quantity of each design, rather than building many copies of the same product.

How additive manufacturing is integrated into product design and build. If the ability to quickly make many versions results in an excess number of prototypes being manufactured and discarded, computer modeling is likely to be a more efficient development strategy. If, on the other hand, additive manufacturing allows a company to create custom products on demand rather than keeping a large inventory of standard products, the strategy reduces waste.

What is 3-D printing?

Most people instinctively understand the concept of 3-D printing. 3-D printers are far more than just a toy for hobbyists, however, and the concept encompasses a variety of techniques suitable for creating products made from a broad array of materials. When implemented correctly, 3-D printing has the potential to revolutionize manufacturing.

The leading commercial applications for 3-D printing include building prototypes and producing custom tooling that is used in manufacturing a variety of products. The ability to print multiple different prototypes allows engineers to inexpensively test out new designs, saving product development cost and encouraging creativity. It's easier to try out new ideas without wasting a lot of time and materials. Printed tooling is a way to create custom parts that cost no more than mass-produced versions.

Additive manufacturing relies on one of several methods to create parts. The choice depends on the material to be printed, performance requirements, and the customer's budget for equipment.

The machines that most people associate with 3-D printing use Fused Deposition Modeling (FDM), in which a filament of material is melted and deposited on a surface in layers. The printers are relatively inexpensive, ranging from tabletop machines for hobbyists to more substantial equipment for industrial use.

FDM printers primarily print various plastics, although the filaments can be infused with metals or other materials. Many use PLA, a biobased plastic mentioned in Chapter 4. Filaments can also be made from recycled plastics, which seems like an especially good idea when making prototypes or sample products that don't need to meet stringent performance specifications.

It may be possible to print 3-D structures using discarded polyethylene. That strikes me as a fantastic way to encourage recycling of plastic bags. If someone can make money by creating plastic filaments from recycled polyethylene, that increases the value of the material and serves as an incentive to convince more recycling facilities to accept polyethylene bags.

Selective laser sintering uses powders as the raw material. As the name implies, a laser sinters (melts) the powders to fuse them in precise locations, avoiding the need to heat the entire part to produce the desired mechanical strength. The process is versatile and can work with polymers, metals, ceramics, and even exotic materials such as food-based powders, but the machines are expensive and best suited to high-end applications.

Many high-end 3-D printers use stereolithography, in which an ultraviolet laser solidifies liquid resins made from photosensitive polymers. The process can print high-quality objects with high resolution and has historically come with a high cost to match. The newest generation of stereolithography-based printers is much less expensive, with models that are even accessible to hobbyists.

As 3-D printing advances, the potential applications go beyond what people currently associate with 3-D printing. As one example, it is possible to control the amount of air incorporated into a material being printed, creating structures with any desired density.

▨ An explosion of printers?

The increased popularity of 3-D printing creates the potential for increased material consumption as the cost of 3-D printers comes down. Just like having an inkjet or laser printer in every home or office provides the convenience of printing documents at a moment's notice, owning a 3-D printer allows individuals and small businesses to print objects whenever they want. This is good news for companies that make 3-D printers, filaments, and powders, but bad news when it comes to reducing waste overall.

The 3D Hubs platform is a network that is designed to alleviate this problem while making manufacturing more local and more efficient. The platform helps customers find a 3-D printer. By making use of the 3D Hubs network, designers can build products closer to where they are being sold, minimizing the costs and resources required to transport them.

Fairphone uses 3D Hubs to create cases for its phones, eliminating the need to pack or ship cases. The approach ties in well with Fairphone's mission. Printing the cases on demand is one more way to reduce inventory and waste.

The 3D Hubs concept can work for both industrial and residential printing. According to 3D Hubs, more than one billion people worldwide have access to a 3-D printer within ten miles of their homes. We shouldn't need millions more printers. 3-D printing is an excellent opportunity to expand the sharing community concept, where local communities share and borrow resources ranging from books to vehicles.

▨ Speeding up the printing process

One problem with 3-D printing is that it is a slow process, best suited for creating custom parts rather than mass-producing many identical pieces. Printing a single product can take many hours.

3-D printing is starting to change. Manufacturers want to move toward higher volume production. To do this successfully, they will need to increase throughput significantly. Printing thicker layers or moving the print heads faster, though, is not the answer, as the result will be low-quality parts that do not meet customer requirements.

The answer for higher volume 3-D printing lies in parallelization—printing many parts in parallel. Professor Jennifer Lewis's research group at the University of Illinois, and later at Harvard, came up with a method to print from up to sixty-four print heads at once. The design needed to meet several challenging criteria. The multi-nozzle structure needed the ability to:

- Withstand the high pressures required to print thick fluids
- Print from a continuous filament

- Achieve uniform flow rates across the nozzle array
- Allow simultaneous patterning of more than one material
- Be scalable for large-area, rapid manufacturing

The researchers produced what is called a bifurcated structure. Fluid from a single parent channel flows into two, then four, all the way to sixty-four individual branches. The structure is machined from low-cost acrylic plastic. Connecting two such structures side by side allows the machine to print two different materials. Lewis's machine can print a 3-D part in less than half an hour. The same design might take an entire day to print using a printer with a single nozzle.

High-volume 3-D printing has not remained confined to university research groups. HP has entered the 3-D printing market, with an eye on speeding up the process. Its Multi Jet Fusion printers can print an array of parts simultaneously. The company claims that its proprietary architecture can dispense thirty million drops of fluid per second. The process appears to be similar to selective laser sintering, but it is much faster. HP's vision includes adding the ability to tailor the properties of each voxel (unit cube, or 3-D pixel) independently. That would allow customers to print products in multiple colors or use different materials in a single part.

3-D printing also presents an opportunity related to HP's standard inkjet printers or those from any other manufacturer. Sometimes a printer stops working because some small plastic part breaks. Frequently the solution is to either buy an expensive replacement part and wait weeks for it to arrive, or abandon the printer entirely by throwing it away and buying a new printer. What if a customer could instead print a replacement part using a 3-D printer at their home or workplace or somewhere nearby? There is no technical barrier for doing so.

This concept of building replacement parts is, of course, valid for products other than printers. In the future, the immediate response to a broken part could be to download a CAD file from the product manufacturer's website and bring it to a nearby 3-D printer to create a replacement in minutes. The product manufacturer would also specify appropriate materials for printing the part. It could be made from the same material as the original part, or from a different material that had the right combination of properties such as strength, weight, and heat resistance.

INTERVIEW   Judy Glazer, HP

Judy Glazer has been working at HP since 1989, through many changes at the company. Her current role is senior director of social and environmental responsibility. She's in charge of figuring out solutions to address social and environmental concerns related to HP's printers and personal computers.

Judy began her journey into sustainability after learning about the proposed Restriction of Hazardous Substances legislation in the early 2000s limiting the use of certain toxic substances in electronics. She was concerned about the impact of RoHS on product design and reliability.

When Judy approached management with suggestions about what needed to be done, they said, "Great! How about if you lead that?" Judy ended up in charge of RoHS compliance throughout HP's supply chain. Her role later expanded to developing a code of conduct for labor, health, ethics, and environment that affects the hundreds of companies that supply materials to build HP products.

HP has strict guidelines regarding materials that are allowed and disallowed in its products. Validation is important. Just because a supplier claims that its materials contain no banned substances, the statement isn't a guarantee. The policy of "trust but verify" ensures that products will be compliant. HP doesn't want to be on the hook if any banned chemicals show up in their products.

Global citizenship was one of the core objectives of HP going back many decades. As Judy tells it, HP employees consider the Sustainable Impact Strategy she and her team designed as a natural extension to that commitment to global citizenship. Environmental considerations affect every aspect of Judy's work, from the raw material supply chain to how customers use HP's products.

Ink and toner cartridges provide an important example of circular economy principles. Companies that make printers have a financial incentive to encourage customers to print as many pages as possible. They want customers to buy more ink and paper and replace their printers more frequently as the printers wear out. But that doesn't have to be their key guiding principle.

HP is well aware of the problem of encouraging customers to go through more ink and paper. The company has held a take-back program since the late 1990s, in which customers return used ink cartridges. The company collects used products, including both consumer electronics and consumables like ink and toner cartridges, from seventy-three countries worldwide for resale or recycling. In 2016, HP recycled over 100,000 tonnes of hardware and 17,000 tonnes of ink and toner cartridges.

The HP Instant Ink program, in which customers register their printers and HP automatically mails them new ink cartridges when theirs are running low, has increased recycling rates by including prepaid return envelopes with the new cartridges. The Instant Ink cartridges have higher capacity than cartridges available in retail stores, resulting in less packaging needed per page printed.

The company has now added a degree of closed-loop processing. Today, the vast majority of cartridges that HP sells incorporate recycled plastic sourced from returned cartridges, as well as other recycled content. HP uses an impressive million or so recycled water bottles every day to make inkjet cartridges. Some of these come from Haiti, where HP pays citizens to collect them, thus providing multiple benefits to society at once. Haitians get a source of income, water bottles avoid becoming part of the waste stream entering the oceans, and the plastic gets recycled into a high-value product.

As Judy explained to me, one of the keys to HP's success in producing high-quality products at a reasonable cost using recycled materials is to have a pure stream of materials entering the process flow. HP collects only its own cartridges, so employees know exactly what is in them and how to disassemble the cartridges and process the plastic for reuse. When they collect used water bottles or plastic clothing hangers, they are also receiving a stream of single-source plastic made from one type of polymer.

Beyond controlling the incoming materials, a lot of engineering and materials science goes into producing a recycled plastic that meets HP's quality standards and using it to manufacture ink and toner cartridges. Judy's team makes sure it all works smoothly.

Judy conveys a sense of optimism about HP. She's encouraged by the direction the company is taking and enthusiastic about promoting greater responsibility and awareness throughout the industry.

They are printing what?

A vast array of materials can be 3-D-printed: plastic and metal are the obvious choices, but printers have built 3-D structures out of concrete, produced food, and even created living tissue. The possibilities are endless, but the most outrageous applications are not practical for commercial use.

In the early twentieth century, Thomas Edison came up with the idea of cast-in-place concrete houses. It's an understatement to say that this was not one of his best inventions. Creating a concrete house with existing technology required expensive metal molds, and the resulting structures were hardly the durable, low-maintenance buildings that Edison was promoting.

But 3-D printing may enable a twenty-first-century version of Edison's concrete homes. After two years of effort, in 2014 Andrey Rudenko completed building his 3-D-printed castle made from extruded concrete. In 2015, he printed a hotel suite, which still stands in the Philippines.

Electronics represent another frontier for 3-D printing. When I covered the printed electronics market and wrote a regular column for a trade publication from 2011 to 2013, the hype surrounding printed electronics was strong. Proponents envisioned thousands of computer chips being churned out like newspapers, using printing methods similar to those in use since the dawn of the twentieth century.

The reality wasn't as promising. Printing thin metal lines to create circuits is straightforward, and by printing them on paper or thin plastic backings, it is indeed possible to print rapidly in high volumes. But creating the wiring is the easy part. Printing the brains of a circuit—the transistors that today are deposited on silicon wafers under extremely stringent conditions to control temperature, moisture, and contamination—remains elusive. There is, however, the potential for printing to contribute to chip manufacturing and reduce the inherent waste involved in certain process steps.

Changing how computer chips are made

Spin coating—depositing a liquid polymer onto a spinning silicon wafer to create a thin layer of the material on the wafer—is a standard process in semiconductor manufacturing of computer chips. The polymer of choice is a polyimide, preferred for its strength and heat-resistant properties.

The spin coating process is a little bit like spin art, only much more advanced and precise. Spin coating covers the wafer with a thin, uniform layer of polyimide, rather than the abstract patterns that a spin art machine creates.

But even though the layer is uniform, the process is very wasteful. More than 90 percent of the liquid that is deposited spins off the wafer. The polymer could potentially be recycled, but semiconductor processing requires extremely pure materials, and even submicroscopic particles in the liquid polymer can cause defects in computer chips. Because of the cost of filtering out these contaminants to reuse the polymer, the excess is usually discarded as hazardous waste.

The polyimides used in semiconductor processing are photosensitive, which means that they react with ultraviolet light. By placing a photomask—very much like a stencil—over the coated wafer and exposing it to UV light, only the exposed areas harden. The rest is rinsed away, losing more material plus the rinse water.

An additive process, where the polyimide is printed in the desired pattern, would use much less material. Why haven't chip makers switched to printing polyimides? To some degree, it's for the same reason they haven't removed solder from their manufacturing lines. The semiconductor manufacturing industry is entrenched, committed to continuing to process wafers the way they have for decades. Companies don't want to invest money in buying completely new equipment and training their staff on how to use it.

This is not to say that the semiconductor industry is not changing. Manufacturers are constantly adjusting their processes to deposit ever-smaller features onto wafers and fit more transistors into the same amount of space. They are innovating, but with the primary goal of creating faster, smaller chips. The goal of decreasing waste is in their field of view, but often in their peripheral vision.

Another problem remains. Printing polyimide today would represent a step backward with respect to feature size. The patterns are not fine enough for the most advanced computer chips. Until the printing technology can print sufficiently small patterns, it won't be competitive for leading-edge computer chips for the latest generation of smartphones. But printing can still be a way to make simpler devices in a less expensive, less wasteful manner.

▨ Unusual methods for additive manufacturing

Additive manufacturing extends beyond 3-D printing. Some companies create parts using additive manufacturing processes that don't resemble printing in the slightest.

Fabrisonic creates 3-D metal parts using ultrasonic welding. Ultrasonic vibration scrubs the oxides off the surface of metals, allowing foils of the same or different metals to bond automatically without added heat. The process does operate at a slightly elevated temperature, but far below the normal melting point of any of the metals involved. The ability to weld dissimilar metals, such as copper and steel, enables structures that couldn't be made using conventional machining.

Fabrisonic takes advantage of a huge computer-controlled milling machine that the company modified to add ultrasonic welding capability. Users upload designs to the machine, and the internal computer controls the motion of the cutting tools to create the desired shape.

The Fabrisonic process combines additive and subtractive manufacturing. Layers of metal foil are welded together and built up additively, and grooves are machined out before welding additional layers. This approach enables structures with internal cavities. The sample products contain an embedded curved groove and a hidden cavity containing tiny metal pellets that rattle when the piece is shaken. That's just for fun, but the process can be used to embed useful things like wires or electronic components.

MX3D in the Netherlands has developed an impressive method of creating 3-D metal structures. Its website features a video of one of its industrial robots drawing metal ropes in the air. It looks like the metal strands appear from nowhere. The process relies on welding, with welding tips at the ends of the robotic arms that bond one drop of metal at a time. The robots build structures with remarkable speed.

When MX3D says it is thinking outside the box, the company means this in a literal sense. Every other 3-D printing technique that I've heard of creates objects within a box-shaped machine. Whether the box fits on a table or is more than ten feet high, like Fabrisonic's machine, objects still need to be built in a confined space. Six-axis industrial robots, however, can travel to a job site.

MX3D's most ambitious project is a 3-D bridge, to be built on-site over a canal in Amsterdam. The project was originally scheduled to be completed in 2017. The concept envisions the robots starting the build on one side of the canal and walking across the bridge segments they have just built to create more of the bridge. The project took a bit longer than expected—a twelve-meter-long bridge span took four robots six months to build. As of mid-2018, testing was ongoing.

As Laurie Winkless pointed out in her 2017 book, *Science and the City*, it is hard to feel confident that a bridge printed in this manner will be sufficiently strong and durable for its intended purpose. Do the welds formed by fusing individual droplets of metal have a uniform internal structure with enough strength and toughness? Still, the MX3D website does show a photo of an employee walking on a much smaller bridge-like structure build by its robots, and the structure doesn't seem to be bending under the man's weight.

INTERVIEW   Dan Schwartz, Clean Energy Institute, and Devin MacKenzie, Clean Energy Testbeds

I had wanted to tour the Washington Clean Energy Testbeds facility at the University of Washington since it opened in February 2017, and in late September of that year, I finally got the chance to do so. The Testbeds are part of the UW Clean Energy Institute (CEI), a research facility that spans multiple departments at the university and focuses on three areas—solar energy, energy storage, and grid integration—chosen because of their importance to society and their ability to scale to commercial products.

CEI and Testbeds are a perfect example of university-industry collaboration, something that has become more prevalent in recent decades. The cross-pollination makes sense, especially for engineering departments. There is certainly a place for research for research's sake, work that expands human knowledge about the world around us. But applied research, aimed at uncovering the link between scientific discovery and the ability to use that knowledge to create products that benefit society, is at the heart of graduate research programs in engineering.

UW understands the importance of applied research. Materials and processes that work well in the lab, at a small scale, will likely face different challenges when they are transferred to real-world scenarios. CEI started as a research institute solely for faculty and students, but Director Dan Schwartz saw a great opportunity to connect with commercial clean energy efforts in the surrounding region. The Testbeds accomplish this goal. The facility provides the missing link: manufacturing at a scale that is compatible with commercial business.

The Testbeds facility is impressive and appeals to my inner materials-science geek. The warehouse-like space, occupying an old sheet metal manufacturing plant near the university, currently inhabits 15,000 square feet of the building, but has room to grow to 90,000 square feet. It is filled with equipment that makes up three different labs, each focusing on one of CEI's primary focus areas.

When I toured Testbeds, I had the opportunity to interview both Dan and Testbeds' technical director, Devin MacKenzie, a UW professor with years of experience as an entrepreneur under his belt. He started the world's first printed electronics company, Plastic Logic, in England at the turn of the twenty-first century.

I wanted to find out how Dan and Devin's work was connected to my central themes of removing toxins and reducing waste. Beyond the obvious goal of replacing fossil fuels with clean, renewable sources of energy, Dan and Devin shared additional insights.

The solar energy lab at Testbeds features a machine that can print solar cells, using a method that is much like printing newspaper. A long roll of plastic sheeting passes through the machine, which deposits silver-laden conductive ink to form electrodes, heats the ink to cure it, and then applies the active layer that converts energy from the sun into electricity. This technology, an exciting application for printed electronics, may very well pave the way toward affordable solar cells.

Printed solar cells use much less material than traditional silicon-based solar cells. The silicon backing, or substrate, on which traditional solar cells are built is sawn from large blocks of silicon. The saw blade is nearly as thick as the layer being sawn off, creating waste from the beginning. Printed cells, in contrast, use a plastic substrate that is produced in exactly the thickness required. The active layers for printed solar cells are deposited on top of the substrate in the precise patterns needed.

Before Devin became an entrepreneur, he earned a PhD in materials science and engineering. His PhD research involved trying to produce colored LEDs based on exotic semiconductors. Although these semiconductors possessed unique properties, they had to be processed at very high temperatures using expensive equipment and some of the most toxic industrial gases and chemicals used anywhere. Some of these materials are so toxic that they are lethal below the minimum detection limits available. If you can detect it, it's too late. The safety procedures in labs that process these gases have to be extremely stringent.

Devin was attracted to the concept of printed electronics because of the potential to make electronic components while avoiding specialty semiconductors that required such complex and hazardous materials and equipment. Just the fact that the printing process is solution-based, meaning that most steps are done in a liquid environment at low temperature with almost no waste, minimizes risk of inhaling toxic gases or dust. Still, some of the solvents used contain volatile compounds that can waft around in the lab. Even within the world of printed electronics, it is possible to make things safer by switching solvents and considering the environmental impact of all the materials used. Devin is committed to looking for those small changes that can yield a safer and more sustainable manufacturing approach.

PART IV

Next Steps

CHAPTER 9

Regulations and Certifications

"If a product doesn't work, it's garbage, and there's nothing less green than creating a product that doesn't function and just adds to more plastic being purchased."
—Jenna Arkin, Earth Friendly Products

"It's important to set medium-term goals so that people aren't saying, 'By 2050, I'm going to be dead, so we can set whatever goal we want.'"
—Ruth Lee, Sustainable Business Consulting

The role of regulations

For better or worse, regulations and laws affect behavior. Regulations that either restrict the use of toxic substances or provide a monetary incentive to switch to more environmentally friendly options are often effective when "do the right thing" messages fail. Laws and regulations often force companies to take action, which some in the business community consider stifling. They feel that such laws restrict innovation or increase costs unnecessarily.

But because proving evidence of cause and effect is difficult, approaches that embrace the "precautionary principle," which emphasizes acting when there is a suspected hazard, serve an important role. In the years that it takes researchers to prove a conclusive link between a specific chemical substance and adverse health effects, a lot of damage may occur.

In an ideal world, manufacturing companies would always consider the health and safety of their employees and customers when deciding what safeguards to install or which materials to use. In reality, profit still often takes priority. The story of industries ignoring public health concerns has happened over and over again since early in the twentieth century, such as radium, tobacco, and oil and gas extraction. Battles over climate change are ongoing even with floods, droughts, hurricanes, and fires breaking all standing records.

There are sound business reasons for embracing healthier business practices. Beyond creating a safer environment for your employees, being proactive enhances reputation and reduces risk.

Companies that take the initiative to invest time and resources in obtaining certifications are in a better position to fairly defend themselves if something goes wrong. If they have been making strides in making their manufacturing processes safer and less wasteful, and they can document their efforts, their customers, shareholders, and the public will be more likely to forgive any missteps.

Sometimes experiencing negative publicity can be a catalyst for change, as it was for Nike. Nike moved past its history of poor working conditions at its factories and remade its image. The company, whose partnership with The Natural Step I discussed in Chapter 2, is now an example of admirable corporate responsibility.

The court of public opinion provides another impetus for companies to switch their tactics. The Occupational Safety and Health Administration (OSHA) was founded in large part because the story of the early twentieth-century radium dial painters became national news.

Public outcry against the dangers of plasticizers containing phthalates convinced chemical companies to develop alternatives. For example, BASF doubled its production capacity of phthalate-free plasticizers in 2014 due to customer demand.

Industrial waste production has in many ways improved since 1960, despite continuing examples of companies trying to escape responsibility for their sins in order to make a profit. Many businesses embrace safer manufacturing processes that create less waste. They know it helps both their reputation and their bottom line and want to do more than meet the minimum standards that regulations require.

▓ Do certifications matter?

Certifications indicate a certain level of quality and show that a company is trying to take steps to be a preferred supplier or to stand out. Although certifications can be helpful, they are no guarantee that a company is doing right by its customers. It isn't wise to trust certifications alone, even though doing so is simpler. Due diligence throughout the supply chain (see page 186) takes more work than checking certification status, but it can help avoid unpleasant surprises later on.

In the mid-1990s I worked for a company that was going through the process of obtaining ISO 9000 certification. The main point was to document all our procedures and make sure that what we were doing matched what we said we were doing. I wrote documentation explaining how we were managing equipment used to do product testing. As far as ISO certification was concerned, it didn't matter whether we calibrated a piece of equipment once a year or once a week, so long as we documented the procedure accurately. What if we only calibrated a sample-testing oven once a year, when the temperature was drifting much more frequently than that? Our data wouldn't be accurate, possibly affecting the reliability of our products, but our facility would have met the certification standard.

Although it's far from perfect, documenting processes is a good first step toward fully understanding how a company conducts its operations. Without knowing the details, it is nearly impossible to know where to look to find areas that need improvement. Going through an ISO certification forces a company to thoroughly examine its practices throughout all different departments.

The ISO certification process has improved since I was involved, aiming to make it more relevant and connected to changes that will help the business as a whole and its customers. Combining ISO certification with lean certification can lead toward an emphasis on continuous process improvements rather than just documenting existing processes.

Still, becoming ISO certified carries a cost, one that doesn't always make economic sense for a business. Around 2012, Smokey Peck, the president of Interwest Paper whose interview appears in Chapter 6, looked into ISO certification for his business. He found that other businesses in his industry weren't certified, which didn't bother customers. No customer had ever asked Smokey if his company was ISO certified. Interwest Paper was already doing most of the steps that would have been required to become certified, but Smokey decided that the stamp of approval associated with certification wasn't worth the cost.

Joining forces

The American Sustainable Business Council (ASBC) serves as an example of the clout that businesses can have if they band together to say that safe, efficient manufacturing and reasonable profits go hand in hand. The ASBC is devoted to promoting triple-bottom-line business practices, emphasizing the need to consider not only profit but people and planet when making business decisions.

The ASBC's advocacy arm advocates for policy change at both the federal and state levels. ASBC asks its members to contact their senators and representatives to express support for certain bills or encourage voting against others.

The Accurate Labels Act was one of ASBC's 2018 targets. This federal bill was sponsored by a group called the Coalition for Accurate Product Labels, which made it sound like an organization promoting product safety. Don't consumers want clear labels so they can understand what's in the products they buy? That's the messaging that the bill's sponsors were highlighting.

But ASBC pointed out that clear labels were not the entire goal. Instead, the act was designed to limit the ability of states to enact labeling requirements that went beyond national standards. Coalition members included a long list of associations representing wide-ranging industries: coatings and sealants, various food products, construction materials, and more. The coalition members had a vested interest in limiting or streamlining the labeling requirements for their products. They didn't want to deal with an array of varying requirements from different states and preferred to avoid excessive labeling.

Some of the points the proponents made sound reasonable. They said that extensive warnings on products about both serious and minor health risks confuse consumers and don't necessarily help people choose the healthiest, safest, or least dangerous option.

The bill mentioned using the "best available science" to determine the appropriate level of warning on a product. That sounds good on the surface. Relying on peer-reviewed studies improves the chance that the research is impartial. But the bill provided a loophole in the case that such studies weren't available. The "best available" research could be funded by the very companies that stand to make a profit selling products that would require warnings, if states were empowered to create and enforce labeling laws.

I'm not convinced that warning consumers about every possible risk is the best approach, and I believe that proposed legislation at the state level should be subject to scrutiny. States are not necessarily acting solely in the best interests of public health either.

Companies making environmentally friendly products opposed the Accurate Labels Act. Their actions are not wrong, but they are not necessarily as altruistic as they seem. Companies in the natural products sector benefit from legislation—whether at the federal or state level—that would require their competitors to post warnings on products or list all the ingredients they use.

State by state

Under the specter of looser regulations from the US federal government, states are stepping up to create legislation, with the hope that their regulations can spread throughout the country. A state-by-state approach makes sense in some situations. Emissions controls on vehicles in California, for example, have been adopted by other states. When I moved into Washington in 2014, I could only bring my car with me if it met California emission standards. Fortunately, I came from California, so the requirement wasn't something that needed to worry me.

California has long been an early adopter of regulations designed to improve safety. Proposition 65, the Safe Drinking Water and Toxic Enforcement Act of 1986, requires labels warning consumers that places or products "contain substances known to the state of California to cause cancer." I'm not convinced that the warnings do a lot of good. When warnings appear everywhere, people become immune to their effect. If cancer-causing substances surround us, how are we supposed to avoid them? It seems inevitable that if we live long enough, something in our environment will give us cancer.

Regardless of the real service to citizens, California continues to lead the way with legislation aimed at restricting certain substances of concern. One example is Senate Bill 258, the "Cleaning Product Right to Know Act of 2017," which passed in California in September 2017. The new law will require all manufacturers of consumer cleaning products to disclose full ingredient lists by 2020 if they want to sell their products in California.

Such regulations affect business nationwide. Manufacturers can't afford to ignore California—it's too large a market—so they will be driven to create compliant products. It doesn't make sense to create different products just for one state, so new labels will likely be appearing nationwide.

Products that are already nontoxic should have a distinct advantage when conforming to Senate Bill 258, even though it is unclear how much weight the average consumer will put on an ingredient list. Not everyone reads the fine print. If the new bill motivates suppliers who use potentially hazardous gredients to change their formulations, however, it will have served a valuable purpose.

The role of local government

Local governments have an important role to play in encouraging (or discouraging) sustainable business practices. In some cities, companies wanting to gain government contracts are graded on their adherence to environmental initiatives. One such city is Portland, Oregon.

Suppliers submitting bids to do work for the city of Portland earn points for sustainable practices such as providing products with a certain percent recycled content or making a less toxic or more energy-efficient product than their competitors. But suppliers need to back up claims with data and follow the guidelines of the ISO 20400 sustainable procurement standard, first introduced in 2017.

The ISO website states that sustainable procurement "involves ensuring that a company's suppliers behave ethically, that the products and services purchased are sustainable and that such purchasing decisions help to address social, economic and environmental issues." The concept can apply equally to corporate and government suppliers.

Portland is far from the only city with policies that encourage environmentally friendly business practices. Cities up and down the West Coast and beyond operate similarly, and the national trend is heading toward rewarding businesses for removing toxins and reducing waste.

The triple bottom line

The companies I admire most are those that truly embrace the concept of the triple bottom line or the three Ps: profit, people, planet. Companies need to create profit, of course, or at least have a goal of doing so. Otherwise, they would be nonprofits or nongovernment organizations. Focusing on people means doing right by employees, customers, and the communities in which they operate rather than only prioritizing returns of shareholders. Focusing on the planet means keeping environmental concerns in mind: limiting pollution, emission of greenhouse gases, and waste.

As David Biello eloquently points out in *The Unnatural World*, people and planet are linked. The survival of the human species should be the ultimate goal of pro-environment efforts. It's not really about "saving the whales." If some combination of pollution, rising ocean levels, natural disasters, and disease were to wipe out the entire human population on the Earth, the planet would continue spinning on its axis and orbiting the sun. Some life forms would survive—probably things like insects, bacteria, and various aquatic species—and the world would continue without us.

More and more companies are getting on board with the concept of triple bottom line, but it can be tricky to avoid this becoming yet another example of greenwashing. Companies want to claim that they are responsible corporate citizens. But saying that they care about the triple bottom line is not enough.

All three aspects of the three Ps need to be balanced, which will often look like profit needs to take a back seat. Depending on where a company starts when it embarks on a three-pronged approach to measuring success, quarterly profits may indeed take a dive as money is invested in improving business practices. Paying workers fairly or redesigning a manufacturing line costs more money than continuing business as usual. Done correctly, however, committing to the three Ps will likely have only a short-term negative impact on profits.

New flavors for corporations

For-profit companies in the US are typically either C corporations (C corps) or S corporations (S corps) based on how they are registered with the Internal Revenue Service (IRS). In contrast with C corps, S corps are limited to one hundred shareholders, all of whom must be US residents.

Small US-based for-profit companies are often registered as limited liability corporations (LLCs) or limited liability partnerships (LLPs), a structure usually popular with law firms. There are more differences between the various types of companies, but the details aren't relevant here.

Since 2010, for-profit companies have been able to take advantage of another option for incorporation. Those committed to the triple bottom line can cement their commitment by organizing as a Benefit Corporation. As of 2018, this option was available in thirty-four states, and an additional six states had legislation pending. Benefit Corporations run under different rules than conventional public companies. Their primary responsibility is not to the shareholders but to their employees, customers, and the communities in which they operate. The legal structure requires executives and boards of directors to consider social responsibility and environmental impact when making any decisions.

Some states, notably Washington, have rejected Benefit Corporation registration as being too restrictive. Companies based in Washington and a few other states allow companies to register as Social Purpose Corporations. Some states allow both Social Purpose and Benefit Corporations.

Incorporating as a Social Purpose Corporation requires businesses to designate some social purpose. They must run operations with that purpose in mind, but the chosen social purpose might or might not consider environmental impact. If the social purpose is limited to, say, donating 1 percent of profits to arts organizations or animal rights, all the company needs to do is make that donation.

B Corp certification

While sometimes confused with status as a Benefit Corporation, B Corp certification through the nonprofit organization B Labs is independent of incorporation. LLCs, S corps, and C corps are all eligible to apply for B Corp certification, as of course are Benefit Corporations.

B Corp certification demonstrates that a company has met strict standards addressing corporate structure, employment practices, environmental impact, and community involvement. Certified B Corps are making a public statement and practicing what they preach, but their corporate legal structure can be of any type.

Customers doing business with a certified B Corp can believe, with high confidence, that the company acts on principles that emphasize the common good. But, unlike Benefit Corporation registration, the company is not legally required to consider the public good.

The B Corp certification process is quite involved, with many detailed questions, and it isn't easy. The answers to those questions do matter. It's not just a matter of completing a simple application and filling in the boxes. Companies must recertify every year and pay an annual membership fee to be part of the B Corp community.

A company must receive a minimum score of 80 points out of 200 to qualify for certification. Even the top-performing companies will likely have scores well below 200, as the maximum is designed to be a high bar to encourage continual improvement. If it were easy to score 100 percent, the incentive to improve would disappear.

Companies that start the certification process often realize that they will need to make many changes in the way they do business to become a certified

B Corp. That realization forces them to either embark on a major effort—which will cost money and compete with the daily demand of running the business—or abandon the goal of B Corp certification.

The choice on how to proceed depends on the level of change required. If the initial assessment points out serious deficits, that presents a chance to re-evaluate whether the path that certification lays out is the one a company wants to follow. I interviewed Janae Lloyd at World Centric to hear a story of successful B Corp certification.

INTERVIEW   Janae Lloyd, World Centric

Janae Lloyd's official title is organizational development manager. Her job is multi-faceted and related to marketing, but the part that interested me was her role leading the B Corp certification process at World Centric. World Centric was an early adopter, having first earned B Corp certification in 2010. The company also became a Benefit Corporation, in 2013. Janae wasn't involved in the initial B Corp certification process since she joined World Centric in 2013, but she led the last few certifications.

Janae says that earning the certification is time-consuming but valuable, with benefits that affect marketing, operations, and supplier relationships. She appreciates the ability to add a B Corp logo on products. Her customers recognize the logo, even if they don't understand everything that's involved in B Corp certification. In the compostable products sector, not having a B Corp certification could be seen as a branding liability.

Certification also creates a pathway for improving a company's policies and processes. Because of updates in the certification assessment, there is always something new to learn. The latest version added a feature that makes it easier for companies to compare themselves to others who have completed the assessment. World Centric's recent score of 124 put it in the top 10 percent.

Even at a company that is devoted to producing environmentally friendly products and creating a positive work environment for employees, there is still room for growth. Janae highlighted supply-chain transparency with manufacturing partners as a focus. Some suppliers provide detailed information on their practices, but others do not. Sometimes suppliers are hesitant to introduce changes to their manufacturing process or business practices, such as adding in a method to reclaim wastewater or better track energy usage.

Becoming a B Corp certified company has allowed World Centric to easily find like-minded companies with whom to collaborate. They prioritize other B Corps when choosing suppliers. Even World Centric's insurance broker is a B Corp.

While Janae appreciates the value of certification, she wishes there were a way to recognize companies that have maxed out the points in specific areas. As an example, World Centric received credit the year it switched to using 100 percent renewable energy at its manufacturing plants. In subsequent years, the company got no credit in that category because it couldn't demonstrate an increase in performance. It isn't possible to use more than 100 percent renewable.

As Janae explained, a company that has maxed out in several areas of assessment can see their score decrease year over year. Does this matter? The company still qualifies for certification, and there's no need to display a score publicly. Still, employees tend to become discouraged and feel less of a desire to take the time to complete the lengthy annual assessment if they don't expect the result to show improvement.

Janae advises companies starting the journey toward B Corp certification not to be discouraged if their score is low. There are probably easy ways to increase it, such as better reporting and tracking or updating official policies to reflect work the company is already doing. Those in the early stages of certification can also learn from existing B Corps by talking to people like Janae who know the certification process well.

The nitty-gritty of GRI reporting

The Global Reporting Initiative (GRI), mentioned in Chapter 1, provides another avenue for formalizing and improving business practices.

GRI issued the latest revision to its reporting guidelines, called the GRI Standards, in October 2016. These guidelines are similar in scope to the G4 guidelines they are replacing but are designed to be much easier to understand and use. Clearer guidelines are a good idea, since sometimes resistance to implementing standards or earning certifications is based on the amount of time and resources that will be required to do so.

The newest guidelines specify exactly which steps are required and which ones are optional, making it harder for a company to hide things. Some guidelines only pertain to certain industries. A mining company needs to report on aspects that a bank would have no reason to mention, for example. The new guidelines should make it easier for companies to create sustainability reports that have been written "in accordance with the GRI Standards," a phrase that customers know to look for.

GRI operates on the premise that the first step in improving operations is to measure what a company is currently doing. Companies that intend to meet all the reporting requirements in the GRI Standards must:

- Collect data from all departments: human resources, manufacturing, facilities, and more.
- Collect data from their entire supply chain to understand where the products and materials that they are buying come from and how they are made.
- Understand what happens to their product or their waste once it leaves their facility, whether that is a purchase by a customer (business or consumer) or delivery to some processing facility to be recycled, discarded, or burned.

The GRI Standards cover a range of environmental aspects, including:

- Materials used to manufacture and package the company's products
- Energy consumption both within and outside the organization
- The total volume of water used and its sources
- Biodiversity impact for sites near "protected areas and areas of high biodiversity value"
- Emission of organic and inorganic pollutants
- Hazardous and non-hazardous waste generation and disposal
- Fines and penalties for noncompliance with environmental regulations
- Supplier environmental assessment

The social reporting section of the GRI Standards covers occupational health and safety, including both injuries and occupation-related diseases.

The information above presents brief summaries. The GRI Standards themselves are much more detailed, and companies often hire independent consultants to help them undertake the vast amount of data-gathering and reporting required.

INTERVIEW   Ruth Lee, Sustainable Business Consulting

I spoke with Ruth Lee, VP at Sustainable Business Consulting (SBC), to get her perspective on how GRI reporting has evolved. SBC performs various consulting services, including advising clients on GRI reporting and helping them implement it.

Ruth has been involved in sustainability her entire career, ever since graduating with a BS in community, environment, and planning in 2008.

In the past few years, Ruth says that changes in GRI reporting practices have focused more on materiality, making sure that reports include the factors that have an important material impact on a business and its stakeholders. Going through the process can force a company to rethink how its policies are affecting employees, customers, and communities. GRI can reach beyond its role as a reporting tool and act as a valuable management tool. By tracking and measuring more aspects of their operations, companies often realize that they need to make changes. In this manner, GRI reporting provides a similar benefit to obtaining B Corp certification.

Ruth told a story about a client with an electronic product that had become obsolete, but they didn't know what was happening with the product once it left their hands. Going through the GRI reporting process forced them to ask questions. The client engaged with supply chain partners to determine what was happening to their now-unwanted products.

The result? The client wrote agreements to make sure their e-waste was disposed of responsibly and not sent overseas. The client even discovered potential new sources of revenue available via selling their old products to organizations that could reuse them.

SBC advises clients to start the GRI reporting process early in the fiscal year to give them time to gather the required data. In the first year, a small company may not be able to collect all the data needed to meet the minimum reporting requirements to create a report that meets the requirements of the GRI Standards. They can still write a sustainability report that provides some level of useful information to stakeholders. The recommended approach, in that case, is to set data-collection goals for the following year, so they are then prepared to create an official report.

Ruth finds that the Carbon Disclosure Project is another useful benchmark. Unlike GRI, where the focus is limited to thorough reporting, CDP gives companies a grade on their sustainability practices and strategy. Goals are more uniform and concrete.

SBC helps with both data collection and messaging around the sustainability journey. They encourage clients to conduct supplier audits, asking suppliers to fill out questionnaires. That way clients can learn where the suppliers stand on questions that appear in the GRI Standards. They can then promote suppliers that hold their values and consider changing suppliers if they aren't happy with the results that their research uncovers.

Ruth has found that going through the GRI can uncover surprising results. For example, a woman-owned business, wishing to answer a GRI question about pay equity for male and female employees, hired SBC to investigate payroll data. The company was shocked to discover that they were paying men more than women. This was a company with more than 1,000 employees. They subsequently addressed the discrepancy between pay levels.

While this example doesn't involve environmental issues, it is still relevant. Even when executives think their company is doing right by its employees or their communities, diving deeper into detailed data may reveal policies that don't line up with a company's stated mission and goals. The best solution is not necessarily obvious. When businesses discover gaps or opportunities to improve, Ruth has pointed out courses of action that her clients haven't considered.

SBC also works with companies that are considering B Corp certification. Ruth finds that clients discover aspects of their business that they might not have initially connected with environmental sustainability. Looking at questions about a company's employee handbook can make executives realize it is missing some important elements. If the elements are already present in the workplace but just not incorporated into the handbook, the fix is fairly easy: just update the handbook.

But sometimes the list of elements points out something the executives hadn't even considered. Adding such a mechanism can pave the way toward both B Corp certification and greening their supply chain. More thorough evaluation of contractors may reveal opportunities to reduce waste.

At the beginning of 2017, SBC was concerned that the US political climate would reduce demand for their services, but they found it was just the opposite. Businesses were deciding that it was more important than ever for them to protect people and the planet.

Companies understand the business case for environmental sustainability and the importance of not being left behind. A sense of positivity has persisted. Companies still operate in a global, interconnected environment and need to meet global regulations. That's good news for Ruth and her colleagues.

Joining forces for good: the value of networks

Forward-looking companies often choose to join networks of similar businesses committed to sustainability goals. By publicizing their membership in such networks, companies gain a reputation for considering environmental issues when making business decisions.

Networks also have more clout than individual companies do when it comes to convincing an industry to change its ways. And not all sustainability-oriented networks require the extensive assessment necessary to become a certified B Corp.

Green America established the Clean Electronics Production Network in 2015. Member companies, which include HP, Dell, and Apple, commit to manufacturing their products using methods that don't expose workers to toxic substances. They pledge to use safer alternatives to some standard chemicals used in electronics manufacturing that have been shown to be hazardous. When such alternatives don't exist, the companies in the network ensure that hazardous waste doesn't poison workers or contaminate the communities surrounding their factories.

Cleaning up the chemical industry

The Responsible Care Initiative is another example of an industry effort yielding better practices. In this case, the target members are companies in the chemical industry, which has received plenty of bad press regarding the inherent hazards of the products it manufactures. Although much of this is warranted, painting all chemical companies as evil is not the right answer.

Society relies on many of the chemicals they produce to make the products we use stronger, weather-resistant, and sometimes actually safer.

The Responsible Care Initiative, launched in Canada in 1984 and adopted in the US in 1988, aims to recognize chemical companies that are leading the way in removing hazards and being good corporate citizens. Chemical companies that have joined the Responsible Care Initiative are demonstrating that they do take their responsibilities seriously, though at times it appears that even those companies take an awfully long time to rid their products of certain toxic compounds.

The initiative covers the safety of products and processes for both chemical companies and their supply partners. The American Chemistry Council, the organization that oversees Responsible Care in the US, requires that all its members participate in the Responsible Care Initiative. CEOs at member companies have agreed to abide by the guiding principles, implement specific safety codes, and publicly report on their performance.

The list of companies participating in Responsible Care may come as a surprise to some people. Familiar names include Chevron, Dow, DuPont, ExxonMobil, and Monsanto. The Ethyl Corporation, the manufacturer of tetraethyl lead, received the Responsible Care Company of the Year award in 2011 and 2012.

Does the presence of these companies that have been accused of polluting the environment and poisoning citizens suggest that the Responsible Care concept is meaningless? It is tempting to say so, but a closer look at the guidelines shows that safety is prioritized. These companies know that the world is watching.

Guidelines cover the following:

- Operating in ways that benefit society, the economy, and the environment
- Implementing safe manufacturing, handling, transportation, use, and disposal processes
- Promoting pollution prevention, minimizing waste, conserving resources
- Communicating risks to stakeholders
- Seeking continual progress toward health and safety goals and reporting performance

While these guidelines are different from concrete goals and subject to interpretation, they are still useful. The Responsible Care Initiative can't stop every potential hazard. It didn't stop Monsanto from producing RoundUp. But without pressure from the American Chemistry Council and similar organizations in other countries, the chemical industry as a whole would presumably pose a much greater danger to public health.

◼ Codes of conduct

Consumer product manufacturers buy chemicals and parts from multiple suppliers. These companies' efforts to behave responsibly will only bear fruit if they continually audit their entire supply chain. Even if a company's manufacturing facilities employ stringent safety measures and avoid the use of toxins, that doesn't mean their products are necessarily free from the problems they are trying to avoid.

In *Green to Gold*, the authors point out multiple examples where companies have been caught off guard, thinking they were being responsible but finding out that somewhere in the supply chain unwanted substances were sneaking in.

Some companies are proactive in measuring and honestly reporting on risks. HP, for example, tracks the hazardous and non-hazardous waste that their suppliers generate. To their credit, their annual Sustainability Reports showed an increase in hazardous waste from 2015 to 2016 as a result of more thorough reporting from a major supplier.

More stringent reporting requirements (see the section on GRI reporting on page 180) are likely to produce data that look worse in 2018 than in 2017. In the long run, however, revealing problems makes it more likely that companies will step up efforts to control waste throughout their supply chains.

Some companies create codes of conduct that all suppliers must meet. The HP Code of Conduct covers practices in a wide range of areas. Suppliers must meet guidelines for environmental permits and reporting, air emissions, pollution prevention, resource reduction, use of hazardous substances, wastewater management, and solid waste generation and disposal. For suppliers who meet the minimum requirements, HP provides incentives for them to go even further and meet more aggressive goals for reducing greenhouse gas emissions or water usage.

DuPont's Code of Conduct focuses on employee health and safety. The code addresses environmental stewardship that embraces the concept of the Responsible Care Initiative in managing greenhouse gas emissions, water and energy use, and waste reduction. The code also discusses compliance with laws and regulations and respect for people.

Mention of hazardous chemical substances is conspicuously absent, probably because it isn't feasible for DuPont to eliminate all substances of concern from its products. The best it is willing and able to do is encourage its employees, and those of its suppliers, to use appropriate safety practices.

Still, DuPont's environmental efforts have convinced at least one influential customer that the company is being a good corporate citizen. Yazaki North

...imental, Health, and Safety Supplier Awards, which were ...Supplier of the Year Awards prior to 2017, recognize its most ...y conscious suppliers. In 2016, DuPont won as the overall ...er of the Year out of eighty-four suppliers.

...North America, a regional arm of the global automotive electronics co... Yazaki Group, audits its suppliers regularly. Its audit process grades sup...ers on multiple factors including energy consumption, community involvement, and reductions of air, soil, and water pollution.

▓ Salmon-safe certification

When you enjoy a glass of your favorite wine, you probably aren't thinking about whether the wine is Salmon-Safe Certified. Why would you? What does it even mean for a wine to be certified as salmon safe, and why does it matter?

The idea of salmon-safe wine doesn't make sense in the same way as dolphin-safe tuna. As far as I know, salmon aren't swimming in ponds or rivers on vineyard property. But there is a connection.

Salmon are not only an iconic symbol of the Pacific Northwest, but they are also an indicator species. This means that if the salmon are thriving, so is the rest of the local ecosystem and vice versa. For those of us living in the greater Seattle area, the health and strength of the salmon population are directly linked to the levels of pollution in Puget Sound. When salmon populations drop, it affects something more important than the price of a fish dinner.

Any farm, whether it grows grapes or other produce, can take actions that affect pollution levels in local waterways, and therefore either help or hurt the health of salmon.

Salmon-Safe Certification is a bit of a big deal. Sites (farms or vineyards) that want to become certified have to adhere to strict standards detailed in a forty-two-page document. The requirements affect irrigation, water runoff, pest management, the location of trees on the property, and more.

Salmon-Safe started in Oregon and has certified more than 350 vineyards in Oregon, Washington, and British Columbia. It is also expanding to California. The Salmon-Safe website maintains a list for those who want to check before they buy. The vineyard certification applies to the land where the grapes are grown, so just because some wines from a specific label are on the list, that doesn't mean every wine from that winery is salmon-safe. The Salmon-Safe organization also produces a wallet card, modeled after the Monterey Bay Aquarium Seafood Watch list, listing certified wines. The card contains many fewer wines than the number listed on the website, suggesting it's in need of an update.

Eventually, the Salmon-Safe Certification may become well known, and people will shop for salmon-safe products just like they shop for organic products. For now, though, many people are confused, like the grocery owner who wondered why she should care about salmon-safe certification when her store doesn't sell fish.

Toward safer products: EPA efforts

Safer Choice, which used to be called Design for the Environment, is an EPA program modeled after the EPA's successful Energy Star program but aimed at green chemistry. It began in 2008.

Products that meet the Safer Choice guidelines must be thoroughly tested, not just for safety but also for efficacy. If a product doesn't work to achieve its desired goal—clean clothing, or stain removal from carpet, for example—it doesn't matter how safe the product is, because no one is going to buy it more than once. A bad experience can sour consumers not only on a particular product but on greener products as an entire category.

The Safer Choice certification process is quite involved and takes about six months. It starts with revealing a complete ingredient list. Each ingredient in a product, except those in a list of pre-approved chemicals, must be sent for an independent review. The EPA screens each category of chemicals. Some products use preservatives, for example. These are allowed if they are among the safest preservatives available and are deemed necessary to extend the shelf life of the product. The presence of neurotoxins, endocrine disruptors, or major allergens, however, will render a product automatically unfit for Safer Choice certification.

For efficacy testing, independent third-party labs conduct the tests, comparing the product against competing conventional and green products. Product packaging must be tested as well. Manufacturers that want to improve their packaging often choose to bottle products in recycled plastic. But recycled plastic sometimes contains unwanted contaminants such as heavy metals. Safer Choice certification requires companies to submit their packaging for independent testing to make sure it does not contain any banned substances.

The Safer Choice program also requires participating companies to engage in continuing research and development to improve their products. Certification only lasts three years, after which companies must retest their products. This level of rigor presents a burden, but as more consumers express a preference for safer products, the certification becomes a more worthwhile endeavor.

As of 2018, the EPA is continuing to shift its focus away from protecting consumers and toward protecting the financial health of companies in certain industries. If consumers are willing to vote with their pocketbooks and buy products with the Safer Choice label, that trend will hopefully override any action the federal government takes to weaken regulations on companies producing personal care and cleaning products.

INTERVIEW Jenna Arkin, Earth Friendly Products

Jenna Arkin is the vice president of innovation at Earth Friendly Products, the company behind the ECOS line of detergents and other household cleaning products. She oversees the innovation team, directing both product formulations and packaging. Jenna didn't start her career at Earth Friendly Products, but she seemed destined to find her way into the family-owned company: she was raised by the company's founder, who started Earth Friendly Products in 1967. Jenna's stepsister Kelly is currently Earth Friendly Products' CEO and president.

Jenna's education is in biochemistry. She took a career detour, earning a master's degree in fashion design and working in the fashion industry for a while, but her chemistry background and the pull of the family business won her back. The company was opening a new facility in Olympia, Washington, and needed a chemist, and they reached out. Now Jenna considers her role that of designing chemistry, blending her creative and scientific passions.

For decades, the company sold its products under the Earth Friendly Products brand, a name that probably sounded unique in 1967 but now shouts "generic green product." Hence the change to ECOS, based on the Greek word oikos. Oikos, which refers to an extended family unit or homestead, is the root behind words like "ecosystem" and "economy." One of Earth Friendly Products' most recognizable and popular products, its laundry detergent, always bore the ECOS label, and now all its products share that branding.

Many ECOS products are designated as Safer Choice formulas, having earned that label through the EPA's rigorous screening process. Earth

Friendly Products was one of the first companies to partner with the EPA when the Safer Choice program was getting started.

In 2015, with green chemistry becoming mainstream and the messaging centering around products that are safe for the whole family, Earth Friendly Products began purposefully seeking Safer Choice certification for more of its products. As of 2018, more than 150 ECOS products were certified. Company policy now states that every new product that launches must be certified as Safer Choice.

When Earth Friendly Products introduced labels with full ingredient lists around 2012, the practice was not common for cleaning products. People were used to seeing ingredient lists on packaged food, but not on laundry detergent or window cleaners. There was initially some pushback, as customers were surprised to see what went into these products, but full ingredient lists are now gaining greater acceptance.

Jenna is pleased by this shift toward more transparent labeling, since she believes that consumers should have full access to information about what is in the products they buy. Some people are allergic even to natural ingredients such as lavender—they should know so they can avoid products that contain known allergens.

Jenna has been involved in lobbying efforts at both the state and federal level. She lobbied for California Senate Bill 258, the cleaning products bill mentioned in this chapter. Given the federal government's reluctance to prioritize health and safety over corporate profits, Jenna believes that a message that promotes "made in the USA" branding will be most likely to resonate. Many customers prefer environmentally sustainable products that are made locally.

Earth Friendly Products continually tries to make its products safer. Preservatives pose a particular challenge. They serve an important purpose in protecting people from toxic microbes, but preservatives are unfriendly to beneficial microbes as well.

While it would be great to be able to eliminate all preservatives, that is not feasible. Removing a preservative but producing a product that will grow dangerous levels of mold is not a good solution. If the company can't eliminate preservatives 100 percent today, they at least want to set goals to limit their use or choose those that pose the lowest risk to the ecosystem, similar to goals for reducing carbon emissions.

Since it isn't always easy to tell whether an ingredient is contaminated, Earth Friendly Products sends new ingredients for independent analytical lab testing before using them. Yes, they trust their suppliers, but they also verify. A supplier might be unwittingly sending contaminated material if the problem started further up the supply chain.

Incremental improvements can be the best approach. Jenna finds that it is important to stay abreast of the latest fundamental research, in addition to conducting company-funded ongoing applied research. A new chemical or material being developed in a university lab today may eventually be able to be produced in sufficient quantities to introduce it into commercial products. Companies can serve as testing grounds for new chemicals and can help researchers launch them into high-volume commercial production.

Sourcing renewable materials rather than petroleum-based materials carries the risk of uncertain availability. Crops are subject to the weather, and some years harvests suffer. Jenna told me that one year, their supply of sage was restricted. Climate change, with its accompanying intense weather patterns, adds to the risk. Still, Jenna considers supply variability as a short-term issue that can be dealt with rather than a long-term issue that threatens her business. Also, sourcing responsibly, from farms in areas where certain crops naturally grow well, helps alleviate the risk that supplies will decline.

Jenna has confidence in her customers' ability to be "forensic consumers," looking up something on her product's ingredient list if they aren't sure what it is or why it's in the product. Earth Friendly Products has developed a program called "Green education for the next generation" to educate schoolchildren, who may become customers. The children make soap and get to see for themselves how the process works.

Jenna finds that the "supersize" mentality in the US can get in the way of making resource-saving choices. For example, ECOS products are available in super-concentrated versions that provide the same amount of cleaning power in half the volume of product. This type of product sells better in Europe, versus in the US where people often have the idea that they should buy the largest bottle they can to save money. Jenna believes that concentrated products are a good idea, but more consumer education is needed for them to catch on in the US.

Earth Friendly Products achieved a milestone in 2017. All four of its facilities—in Olympia, Washington; Cypress, California, near Los Angeles; Addison, Illinois, near Chicago; and Parsippany, New Jersey, near New York City—are completely carbon neutral, water neutral, and platinum zero-waste-to-landfill certified.

Spreading out its facilities throughout the country allows the company to source more of its supplies, such as bottles, locally for each facility. It also makes shipping more efficient, limiting the length of shipping routes needed to distribute its products into stores.

Of the four markets, Jenna says that the Pacific Northwest is the easiest to manage when it comes to recycling. The other regions are supportive of recycling efforts, but composting is a different story. Earth Friendly Products composts at each of its facilities, but in New Jersey, the employees had to be educated about what composting even was.

The platinum zero-waste-to-landfill certification does not require absolutely zero waste. Ninety-five percent is sufficient and still impressive. In a 100,000-square-foot facility, Earth Friendly Products sets out one trash bin per month, much less than an average US household of four living in a 2,000-square-foot home.

Achieving platinum certification has required careful management of the supply chain. The company doesn't bring anything into its facilities unless they know how the packaging is going to be handled when they're done using the ingredient. Every shipping container received, for example, needs to be reusable or recyclable. Bottles for ECOS products contain a high percentage of post-consumer recycled plastic. Pallets of bottles come secured with various types of plastic straps. By separating the different varieties of plastic, the straps can be economically recycled.

Because the company makes cleaning products that are almost food-grade quality, safe product handling requires workers to wear protective gloves to prevent contamination of the products. The disposable nitrile gloves were becoming a problem getting in the way of the zero-waste-to-landfill goal. The solution? Finding a recycling facility that collects the used gloves and turns them into park benches. Yes, it's downcycling, but since the alternative is the landfill, it's probably the best option available.

Jenna embraces the aspect of today's connected world that encourages web-based peer review, believing that companies like hers will rise to the top. Customers talk, and if a supposedly green product doesn't work well or causes an allergic reaction, that product is not going to succeed in the open market.

Jenna believes that green products shouldn't be a luxury and understands the importance of pricing that doesn't vastly exceed that of conventional brands. Vertical integration allows Earth Friendly Products to control costs and sell to average Americans.

CHAPTER 10

Taking Action

"Sustainability touches every sector."
—Saman Baghestani, SHIFT

*"Walmart sells so much stuff that they can make
a difference just by changing one product."*
—Sam Hopkins, EcoSheep

▦ Our many roles

Through reading this book, I hope you have learned at least a few new things. Perhaps you didn't know where metals and plastics come from, or if you did, you didn't know how they could be made in less wasteful ways. Perhaps you learned about companies you didn't know existed and how they are innovating to make practical use of materials that would otherwise go to waste. Perhaps you gained a new perspective on the role of laws and regulations or appreciation for the challenges facing companies whose reputation has been less than stellar.

Knowledge is good, but without action, it fades into the background, and we move along doing things the way we always have. While I hope you have enjoyed reading and learning, what I really hope you will do is let your newfound knowledge inspire you to change something in your life. Options range from adopting new habits around recycling to working for a company that better aligns with your values.

My business cards read, "How are you changing the world?" The phrase intends to emphasize changes that will improve people's lives. The email subscription button on my website encourages visitors to subscribe to my materials blog to "Learn something new that might spur you to action."

We all play many roles in our lives: citizen, consumer, employer, employee, volunteer, family member. Some of these roles afford us a particular advantage or disadvantage when deciding to remove pollutants or reduce waste. This chapter looks at each in turn and offers suggestions for ways to make a positive difference.

We are all citizens

Wherever you live, you are a citizen of the country in which you were born or the country in which you reside, or in some cases, both. For those who are old enough and not otherwise barred, the status of citizenship conveys the right to vote and the right to run for office.

In the US, we can choose how to react to the prospect of the federal government removing restrictions on industries that pollute and contribute to wasteful practices and increased burning of fossil fuels. We can decide that the situation is hopeless and do nothing. We can pretend that if we wait, the situation will take care of itself. We can take the view that it's someone else's problem or that it won't affect us personally. This is not an uncommon viewpoint, but it's not the best approach.

Instead, consider reacting to the loosening of federal restrictions by supporting state and local legislation aimed at improving public health and safety. We can vote for candidates who support responsible business practices.

Be an informed citizen. Whether the issue is a proposed ban on single-use plastic bags in your city or statewide changes in the tax structure for businesses with manufacturing facilities in your state, learn about upcoming legislation. The more you know, the better you can decide how to vote or whether to do more than merely cast your ballot.

If you have a strong opinion on an issue, volunteer your time by:

- Gathering signatures to get a measure on the ballot
- Signing online petitions supporting or opposing a measure
- Calling your neighbors to encourage them to vote
- Calling your congressional representatives at the state or federal level and asking them to support or reject a pending bill
- Joining a campaign to elect a candidate whose positions align with yours

For those inclined to get more deeply involved, there are many opportunities, from volunteering for a committee or planning commission in your city to running for office.

If you live outside the US, your country's government probably isn't trying to reverse decades of progress on public health and safety. If you're in the US and reading this book many years after 2018, the situation in this country may have changed. Regardless, the advice to be an informed citizen and volunteer your time supporting legislation that improves the health of your community remains valid.

When you're the CEO

The journey of World Centric demonstrates how to impact more people as a for-profit business than as a nonprofit organization. World Centric started as a nonprofit but quickly realized that the demand for their compostable food containers was considerable. The organization began at a time when customers were aware of the problems with Styrofoam and willing to shell out money for an alternative. By transforming itself into a for-profit Benefit Corporation, World Centric can make money by selling products. It then invests some of those profits in projects benefiting communities around the world.

Closing the Loop experienced a similar journey in the EU, transforming itself from an NGO to a social enterprise corporation. A market for used phones provided a business opportunity that aligned with the company's mission.

If you own a small business, you get to call the shots and determine how you want to implement sustainability. Small and privately owned businesses have an advantage over public companies, in that they don't have to answer to shareholders. You can prioritize sustainability goals by choosing suppliers based on quality or ingredient lists, without worrying about how that will affect the stock price. You can choose which certifications will be worth the investment of time and money required to obtain them.

On the flip side, small businesses don't benefit from economies of scale that keep costs down and enable larger margins. Suppliers who produce relatively small quantities of products have to pass an increased cost per item to their customers to stay in business. Large companies are in a position to lobby suppliers for discounts on environmentally friendly materials or products in exchange for publicity or a promise of regular orders. Small businesses do not share this advantage.

Publicly held companies face different concerns. If you own a public company and are responsible to a board of directors and shareholders, they expect to see a return on their investment. Profit is always important. You can, however, still sell the advantage of considering the triple bottom line. If your company is large enough, your decisions can sway an entire industry, as the quote about Walmart at the beginning of this chapter points out. Even if becoming a Benefit Corporation is not a realistic option, you can consider B Corp certification or using GRI reporting as an incentive to improve business practices.

Approaches to sustainability will necessarily differ by company, depending on what the top executives believe to be the most important values, those that their stakeholders will care about. Culture starts at the top, meaning that executives need to take ownership of the company culture, brand, and image and how they communicate that culture to employees and customers.

The importance of corporate culture is true for small businesses and large public companies alike. If you are in the executive suite, what message are you sending with your business practices?

If you want to lower your company's carbon footprint and reduce waste by addressing plastics usage, for example, you should consider the following:

- How does your company use plastic, and does it make sense to replace disposable or durable plastic products with those made from other materials?

- What does your waste stream look like? How much is discarded into the trash, recycling, or compost bins each week or year?

- Are employees and customers aware of recycling and composting processes? Do they know what to toss where? If not, clearer signage and employee training will help.

- Can you find opportunities to buy lower quantities of disposable plastic, or switch to compostable products if there are appropriate composting facilities in your city?

- Analyze your supply chain. Can you buy products that use less material, or buy products that last longer, whether they are made from plastic or other materials?

- If you ship products, examine how you are packaging them and whether you can reduce packaging, use more recycled content, or shift to reusable packaging, while still ensuring that your products arrived undamaged.

It will take some digging to figure out the best answers to the above questions. You need to carefully examine possible tradeoffs when swapping out materials or suppliers.

For companies in industries that generate toxic emissions or hazardous waste, the issues are much more complicated. Still, it is possible to limit the hazards through implementing more stringent safety procedures or swapping out chemicals for less toxic ones that can still achieve the desired goals for product performance.

In the second instance, nontoxic chemicals may cost more per gallon, but a thorough analysis could still show a cost savings. Hazardous waste disposal costs money. Even if the analysis doesn't directly demonstrate lower cost, it is possible to make a case for changing materials. Cost pressures are real, but businesses that create products sold directly to consumers can appeal to those who prefer an environmentally friendly product and are willing and able to pay a bit more.

INTERVIEW Ryan Kellner, Mighty-O Donuts

"The donut is just the widget." If this remark seems unusual, that's because Ryan Kellner is not a typical donut shop owner. Ryan's goals for Mighty-O Donuts, a small chain based in Seattle, go beyond making donuts or making a buck. He started out wanting to create a sustainable business, although at the time he didn't think of it in precisely those terms. Ryan's career has taken an unusual path, beginning with a degree in geology and a focus on environmental geology and resource management. Those studies opened his eyes to look at the natural environment in a new way.

Much of geology centers around mining. The high-paying jobs for geology majors have historically been in the mining or oil and gas industries. Ryan notes, "The true wealth comes from the planet," providing work for those who can efficiently find and extract the world's mineral resources. Ryan's interests slanted toward environmental work and water conservation, but he initially went where the jobs were, traveling to do geophysical surveys.

Ryan now commutes by bicycle and public transit. His love for the outdoors and environmental bent fits in better with the Pacific Northwest lifestyle than with being the owner of a donut shop, but starting a business was always at the back of his mind. When he came up with the idea of donuts, he knew he wanted to incorporate his values, so he decided to differentiate his business by making donuts with organic, vegan ingredients.

Back in 2003 when Ryan opened his first donut shop, he had to create his own supply chain. Sourcing organic ingredients wasn't as easy as it is today. The industry wasn't quite ready. Federal rules for certified organic foods didn't yet exist, though the concept was alive and well in a few regions of the country.

Ben & Jerry's stood as an inspiration for Ryan, starting when he read the founders' book *Ben & Jerry's Double-Dip*. He also read everything he could from Paul Hawken, author of *The Ecology of Commerce* and many other books about pairing sustainability with success in business.

When Ryan was starting his business, he tried an industry-standard product called donut frying shortening, a blend of hydrogenated corn and soy oils combined with various additives. Ryan found the stuff disgusting. Washing it off of clothing was impossible. And, to get his donuts into stores like Whole Foods, Mighty-O couldn't use hydrogenated oils. He looked for another option and discovered palm oil.

When the food industry moved away from trans fats, it turned to palm oil because that was similar to the hydrogenated oils they had been using. There was suddenly a huge demand for palm oil. But, as with conflict minerals, palm oil comes with a dark side involving both environmental and social issues. People in Indonesia were forced to give up their land if someone wanted to bulldoze it and grow palm trees. They ended up becoming slaves on their own property.

At the time, Ryan was frying his donuts in organic palm oil. When he investigated his sources, he was relieved to learn that the palm oil in his stores wasn't coming from Indonesia. It came from South America, from companies with sustainable practices, using land that was already farmland rather than cutting down old forests. Business owners today have more choices than was the case fifteen years ago. According to a 2017 report by the Roundtable on Sustainable Palm Oil, more than 20 percent of palm oil worldwide is sustainably and responsibly produced. Much of that does come from Indonesia. Still, there is room for improvement in addressing practices at the companies providing the other 80 percent.

Packaging presented Ryan with another challenge. "It's hard to avoid any plastic, but we try our best." Creating a compostable box proved to be a problem. He had to worry about details such as inks and coatings and ended up creating his own box. For small orders, he puts donuts into plain paper bags. The company continues to audit its supply chain as new products, such as compostable cups, become more widely available.

Back in the early days of his business, when there was no citywide program to pick up compost, Ryan took food waste home with him to compost in his backyard. Many years later, when the city of Seattle began requiring quick-service restaurants to compost, Mighty-O was already ahead of the game. And at the end of each day, the stores offer free leftover donuts to nonprofits to minimize food waste.

At Mighty-O Donuts, there is no trash can for customers. They have achieved zero waste to landfill on the consumer side. The stores don't sell bottled water, even though it would provide an easy extra revenue stream. Ryan faces limitations, though. For example, some bulk products are shipped to the stores wrapped in plastic. Employees have to wear disposable gloves for safe food handling. Still, the amount of garbage that the donut shops generate is as low as they can reasonably achieve.

As Mighty-O Donuts grows and adds more stores, Ryan sees that as an opportunity to help more farmworkers. But Ryan is not a slave to a certain ideology. As an example, although the donuts are vegan, the stores sell milk. Ryan wants to support customers who are vegan but doesn't want to alienate those who aren't. He still intends for the stores to remain vegetarian, though, so customers who want donuts with bacon will have to go elsewhere.

Influencing your employer

If you work at a company, your ability to influence corporate practices is related to your job responsibilities and the size of the business. In many companies, the higher your relative rank, the better positioned you are to convince your company or department to change suppliers or package products more efficiently.

In a small company, it can be easier for any employee to have an influence. Company executives are more accessible, as opposed to some larger companies that have a hierarchical structure in which the chances of a message reaching the CEO seem remote. Without the top executives on board, company policy isn't going to budge.

Employees who care about environmental issues should understand how their company is positioning itself. Does the company prioritize addressing environmental problems because it is the right thing to do for the future of society regardless of short-term cost? Or is the focus more on doing the minimum required to give the impression of being a good corporate citizen? Are there specific incentives or penalties driving change toward new policies or procedures? Legal restrictions or the prospect of reduced taxes both exert pressure to adapt.

If you work for a company where the executives support a triple-bottom-line approach and value all aspects—people, planet, and profit—you can expect that your supervisor will listen and consider suggestions that will improve any of these aspects. Hopefully, your work environment is such that you feel empowered to propose suggestions based on your knowledge of current practices at your workplace.

The more you know, the more effective you can be in instigating change. Be aware of common industry-wide practices and those of the most forward-looking companies in your industry. Learn whether city or state laws support or restrict the ideas you wish to implement. Armed with this knowledge, you have a greater chance at success.

If, on the other hand, you work at a company where profit is king and the executives have little patience for changes that cut into sales margins, your situation looks different. In this case, I see three choices: accept the way things are, look for a job at a different company, or propose radical changes anyway. If you choose the third option, realize that doing so will probably not earn you brownie points and might get you fired.

Positive trends across industries

Does the company where you work embrace less wasteful, more sustainable practices and policies that support a triple bottom line? If it doesn't do so today, chances are increasing that it will soon. I see progress when I browse the newsletters arriving in my email inbox every week. More companies are going public with commitments to corporate responsibility, environmental stewardship, and the health of their employees and customers. These companies span industries as varied as food and beverage, textiles, construction, electronics, hospitality, and even petrochemicals and mining.

Yes, companies realize that publishing sustainability reports is a way to gain positive publicity. But the reports are public, and anyone can read them.

Before the latest revisions to GRI reporting, people needed to read between the lines to consider what was left out in addition to what was included. My work writing and editing content for businesses falls into the realm of technical marketing. I know very well that if a company's product doesn't excel in a particular area, it's best not to mention it and hope that customers will focus instead on the positive benefits the company chooses to highlight.

Now when sustainability reports are published "in accordance with the GRI standards," companies can't omit a section where their performance isn't stellar. True, they can lead with their best foot forward. But the report still needs to include all the warts.

Reading the fine print is important. A 2017 report from Kinross, a gold mining company, states that the report is "based on the new GRI Standards and has been prepared to be largely in accordance with the Core option of reporting." This is not, therefore, an official GRI report, and the company may have neglected to report on elements where their performance is lacking.

Regardless of the details, I find the progress encouraging. Even if some companies are merely jumping on a trend by writing sustainability reports or adding "sustainability" or "environment" pages to their websites, it's a good trend to be joining.

We are all consumers

Regardless of whether you run a company, work for a for-profit business or a nonprofit organization, or have retired from professional life, you are a consumer. In that role, you make dozens of choices every week about what products to buy and where to buy them. You can also choose what not to buy and how to dispose of stuff when you're done using it. Your role as a consumer gives you the power to vote with your pocketbook.

I interviewed representatives of businesses making nontoxic cleaning products, donuts made with vegan ingredients, and lanolin-based bicycle lubricant. Those companies are doing a thriving business because consumers like the products they offer and believe in the message behind them. This message wouldn't have resonated with nearly as many people a generation earlier.

All but a fringe segment of the population would have laughed about the concept of vegan donut ingredients in the 1980s—if they even knew what that meant. Between 2015 and 2017, Mighty-O Donuts opened three new locations.

When I was growing up, no one I knew cared or thought about whether cleaning products were dangerous or toxic. Now ECOS brand cleaning products carrying the Safer Choice seal appear in mainstream stores including Costco, Target, and Safeway. The stores wouldn't carry these products if customers weren't buying them.

Consumer behavior can shape corporate actions. From bringing reusable bags to the store even in cities that don't ban plastic bags to choosing products that come with less packaging, you send a message. One customer won't convince a company to change the packaging on its products, but thousands of customers will. More and more products boast that they now come with less packaging.

It is, of course, important to look closely. Some products come packaged in plastic for sanitary reasons or to save weight in shipping. As we saw with the story of wooden versus plastic shipping crates in Chapter 6, sometimes plastic is the better choice from a sustainability perspective. As consumers, we can examine packaging to learn about whether it is made from recycled or recyclable plastic or both.

In addition to buying less packaging, we can learn about options for recycling and composting in our communities. Figuring out what is and isn't recyclable can be challenging, but taking the time is worthwhile. We don't want our recycling efforts to contaminate the recycling stream accidentally.

I will admit that I have not always been as aware of issues surrounding toxins in the products I buy or the waste inherent in producing, packaging, and shipping them. My awareness, already growing before I began writing this book, has increased as a result of my research. I have made changes.

- I already composted at home—a task made easier because my city provides a small compost bin and accepts all types of food waste into the large yard waste container—but now I think about what I'm putting into the compost other than food and make sure I don't include any coated cardboard packaging.

- Because I compost, my garbage disposal mostly stands idle, and I haven't had any problem with clogs. When drains in my house do clog, I don't pour caustic cleaners down the drain. It's not fun, but manually taking apart and cleaning out the pipes under the sink takes care of the problem.

- I put leftover food into reusable glass or plastic containers rather than wrapping it in plastic wrap or putting it into a disposable zipper-top bag. I also write dates on the containers to limit the amount of food I throw away.

- I wash out used containers and, after checking that they won't contaminate my city's recycling stream, toss them into the recycling bin.

- I no longer recycle store receipts because I learned that they are coated with BPA or BPS and aren't recyclable. I throw them away, or, better yet, opt out of paper receipts in the first place and choose an electronic receipt when the option is available.

My behavior is far from perfect, especially compared with what I read in the Zero Waste Seattle Facebook group feed. I buy products that come in plastic bottles. My family members bring home plastic bags from the grocery store too often. These do, however, come in handy for bagging cat waste from the litter box.

Sometimes the extremes to which people in the Zero Waste group go surprise me, but I applaud their efforts to reduce waste. I knew that baking soda worked as toothpaste, but it never occurred to me to wash my hair with it or with apple cider vinegar. I learned that both baking soda and vinegar work in place of shampoo, but I don't fancy having my hair smell like vinegar. I imagine that some zero waste proponents have trained their cats to use the toilet. My cat is twelve years old, and I'm not going to try.

Regardless of where you are on the spectrum of caring about the safety and environmental sustainability of the products you buy, I suspect there is room for improvement. Only you can decide how much time you want to devote to making changes in your lifestyle and habits and how much pressure you want to put on the companies that make the products you enjoy.

I hope that the information in this book has helped you decide how to focus your efforts at home where they will make the most difference.

The importance of location

When considering steps to reduce waste in your community or remove toxic products from the business where you work, location makes a difference. Are you preaching to the choir or making suggestions that people around you will interpret as too costly or negatively associate with counter-culture hippies?

I have lived my entire life in the bubble of the West Coast. Sustainability is an easy sell in the Puget Sound region—the greater Seattle area—where I have been since 2014. Before I moved here, I lived in the San Francisco Bay Area, in a state that led the country in requiring businesses to pollute less and conserve more. Companies in my part of the country recognize that publicizing their sustainability efforts, whether that be using compostable containers or powering and heating their buildings solely with renewable energy sources, will attract customers who value these efforts.

Is the same true for companies based in the Midwest or Southeast areas of the US or that have manufacturing facilities or retail stores in these regions? Ryan Kellner, the owner of Mighty-O Donuts, was at a dinner event put on by Sustainable Seattle, where his company was receiving an award. The emcee congratulated the audience for doing the right thing and talked about the importance of spreading the message across the country to regions where sustainability isn't yet popular.

My limited research suggests that the message is indeed spreading. The idea of reducing toxins and hazardous waste is an easier sell in certain markets, but companies throughout the country are finding that their customers do care. The messaging needs to be slightly different, appealing to saving money or keeping their family safe rather than saving the planet, but there is a market for environmentally friendly businesses and products in regions far from either coast.

If an environmentally friendly product is reasonably priced and does the job better than a product made from materials that are toxic and wasteful, customers all over the country will buy it. Sam Hopkins, the CEO of EcoSheep whose interview appears in Chapter 4, says that sales of his lanolin-based bicycle lubricant are not at all limited by geography. Adjusting for population density in various regions, he sees no concentration in the typical eco-friendly bubbles.

Despite the evidence that environmentally friendly practices aren't restricted to regions where the message has long benefited from public support, limitations do exist. For example, composting programs aren't available in many cities, and some regions compost only yard trimmings and food waste but not compostable packaging. The Seattle area is ahead of the curve with the Cedar Grove facility, which accepts all types of food waste and compostable packaging and turns it into compost. Laws in the city of Seattle prohibiting disposable packaging that isn't compostable encourage businesses to provide single bins for customers to deposit both food waste and serving ware. The goal is diverting as much waste as possible from local landfills.

Oregon has taken a different approach than its neighbors to the north and south, prioritizing the quality of finished compost over landfill diversion. Composting facilities in the state are not set up to handle most compostable service-ware and the composting industry there sees these products as a problem. The city of Portland prohibits packaging or food-service ware in its compost, only allowing uncoated cardboard pizza boxes, coffee filters, tea bags, and paper products in addition to food waste. While research studies show counterintuitive results about the environmental impact of compostable plastics, potentially less-damaging ways of making these products are in development (see page 68). In the long run, it isn't clear whether Seattle's or Portland's approach should prevail.

In cities without composting programs, simply setting out a container to collect compost won't help. Unless a business has space and resources to set up on-site composting or a homeowner wants to build a backyard compost bin, vegetable scraps are destined for the kitchen sink disposal or the garbage can.

Regardless of where you live and work, however, online tools can point you toward resources that apply to your situation and answer the questions you are asking. The Earth911 website provides information about recycling and composting options by location in North America. But this is only one example of the vast array of information out there addressing a variety of issues and questions. An online sustainability forum led to my interview with Saman Baghestani, who manages an organization devoted to simplifying the search for information from anywhere in the world.

INTERVIEW Saman Baghestani, SHIFT

Saman Baghestani is the project manager of SHIFT.Tools, an online platform that curates resources for learning about and incorporating sustainability into business practices. The SHIFT website links visitors to websites that will provide the details they need, saving them the time it would take to conduct multiple searches and sift through the information.

Saman's participation in the BASIC network, originally the Boston Area Sustainable Investors Consortium but now re-branded as Building a Sustainable Investment Community, led him to his role with SHIFT. Colleagues in the BASIC network told Saman about SHIFT in late 2016, when the fledgling website was looking for a product manager. The opportunity seemed tailor-made for Saman, allowing him to combine his passion for sustainability and corporate responsibility with a background in program management. The MIT Sloan School of Management agreed, so they hired Saman to manage SHIFT, the latest project coming out of its Sustainability Initiative.

The name SHIFT acts both as an acronym—sustainability, help, information, frameworks, and tools—and as a descriptive term for a project aimed at shifting people's mindsets and practices. Saman gets excited about connecting website visitors with sustainability tools, helping them navigate the vast array of information floating around the internet and find what they need. The website features a chatbot, allowing Saman to potentially interact with every website visitor and also keep a log that tracks areas of interest.

Saman pulled up his records and gave me a glimpse into recent requests, which included:

- A pulp and paper company in India wondering how to engage their employees around health and safety issues
- A beverage company looking to understand how consumers feel about recyclable bottles
- Multiple businesses with an interest in circular product design, searching for materials to use to increase recyclability
- Students researching environmental topics
- Teachers searching for ways to educate their students
- Investment groups wanting to measure the risk of portfolio companies for environmental and social issues
- Cities wanting to develop a climate action plan or improve water stewardship
- Businesses of all types looking to achieve net zero waste

For those interested in the circular economy, SHIFT will direct them to the Ellen MacArthur Foundation. Investors can find links to Thomson Reuters' environmental, social, and governance data. City managers can look to San Francisco or Melbourne, Australia, as examples.

I noticed that SHIFT appears to emphasize the fashion industry, and Saman told me that this focus is a purpose-driven effort. Fashion is both very consumer-facing and also resource-intensive. SHIFT wants to direct the industry toward solutions that will make recycled polyester more cost-competitive and support coalitions driving progress toward providing workers around the world a living wage.

SHIFT is based in the Boston area, but 60 percent of website visitors come from outside the US. Traffic comes from the expected places—Canada, Germany, Australia, the Netherlands—but also from less obvious locations such as South America. Saman encourages participation from everyone, no matter their geographical region or industry sector.

▓ **Through the generations**

Of the many roles we play in our lives, one of those is family member. Perhaps you are at the stage of life where the word "family" brings to mind your parents and siblings. Maybe you are a parent or grandparent. Regardless of your age and family situation, you should be concerned about the future of this planet, which means the future of the human species. Parents of young children will be especially concerned about toxins in baby bottles or sippy cups, but even if we aren't parents or if our children are grown, we should still be aware. Poisons are especially dangerous for young children, but adults are not immune.

I remember reaching the age of eighteen or so and thinking I no longer needed to worry about becoming one of those missing children whose names and faces appeared on milk cartons. By the time I became a mother, milk cartons no longer featured those photos, but I recognized my responsibility in keeping my children safe. Fortunately, I nursed each of them for more than a year, reducing their exposure to BPA, which hadn't yet been eliminated from baby bottles. Still, as Michael SanClements points out in his book *Plastic Purge*, BPA exposure creeps in from many sources. My children have grown up to be reasonably healthy, but they have been exposed to carcinogens that could lead to cancer decades from now. I have been exposed to many of the same toxins and some different ones.

But the situation is far from hopeless. I believe that it makes sense to be vigilant, but pressure for greater corporate responsibility is changing. The e-newsletters that land in my inbox every week include stories about companies improving their business practices and reputations. Sustainability reporting is more comprehensive and more uniform, thanks to updates in GRI reporting, and more companies than ever are issuing annual sustainability reports that follow the guidelines. The reports highlight reduced energy and water use for manufacturing and operations, more reliance on renewable energy sources, increased use of recycled materials, and more.

When the cynic in me worries that some businesses are primarily changing their policies or products to improve their bottom line, I remember that when more sustainable manufacturing increases profit, that's a good thing. Profit is one of the three Ps, after all, and I want responsible companies to stay in business. The trick is to read behind the lines and encourage changes that achieve the benefits they promise. When removing a toxic chemical, are manufacturers replacing it with something that is potentially just as dangerous, such as swapping BPs for BPA, or are they finding an alternative that is proven to be safer? Do efforts toward zero waste to landfill involve using less material overall?

Excess plastic consumption and the plastic trash problem received lots of attention in 2018, bringing the issue into the limelight. I doubt that disposable packaging will disappear in my lifetime, but progress toward that goal is possible. It is important to proceed with caution. Rather than replacing all conventional plastics with biobased plastics and claiming success, manufacturers need to consider the impact on human health and the environment that increased bioplastics production will cause and choose bioplastics that don't cause more problems than they solve.

The policies in China that stem the flow of recyclables, trash, and e-waste to that country will change the way cities in North America and Europe manage recycling. Ideally, our infrastructure will improve, allowing more materials to be recycled safely and efficiently at a cost the market can bear. New technologies for processing e-waste, along with manufacturing practices that require fewer and less-toxic resources, will, hopefully, make society's reliance on electronics less damaging to people and the environment.

Ultimately, we need to trust scientists. We should encourage businesses to rely on independent research to ensure that the new products that they introduce will meet customers' needs while reducing the resources required to manufacture them and minimizing health risks. Concern about the health of people and our environment has become mainstream, and choices of materials play an important role in ensuring a safer future for the generations who will follow us. Businesses that understand their responsibility deserve the support of customers who want to promote more sustainable, less wasteful manufacturing. When we use our power as citizens, consumers, and workers to affect what materials go into the products we enjoy and how those products are made and used, everyone benefits.

ACKNOWLEDGMENTS

When I first came up with the idea for writing this book in early 2017, Leo Novsky responded enthusiastically and said we should start a Meetup group to support our journeys. Our weekly meetings of the Eastside Nonfiction Book Writers inspired me to reach out for my first interview, reorganize the planned content in the book, and commit to making it a reality.

Nina Amir's Write Nonfiction in November, a nonfiction version of the popular National Novel Writing Month (NaNoWriMo), convinced me to buckle down and finish my first rough draft. It had many holes, and I had plenty of work ahead before I would be willing to show my manuscript to anyone, but completing a 50,000-word draft made me realize that there was no turning back.

I have had the privilege of interviewing many inspiring individuals while researching this book. Talking with these people gives me hope for the future in an uncertain world. Thanks to the following people for sharing their stories: Jenna Arkin, Saman Baghestani, Mallen Baker, Joost de Kluijver, Joe Fjelstad, Jeff Frost, Judy Glazer, Peter Holgate, Samuel Hopkins, Brion Hurley, Ryan Kellner, Ruth Lee, Janae Lloyd, Devin MacKenzie, Andrew Maxey, Smokey Peck, Daniel Schwartz, Mark Stephany, and Kjell van Zoen. Thanks to Richard Eidlin, who introduced me to some of the people I interviewed.

Several beta readers gave me valuable feedback on the second draft of my manuscript, from suggesting that I combine some chapters to flagging paragraphs that needed more explanation. Thanks to Bruce Follansbee, Steve and Sofia Freer, Christine Hoeflich, Steven Howard, and Paul Osborn for your helpful suggestions. I have to acknowledge David Allaway, whose presentation in a webinar on recycling and composting prompted me to contact him late in the editing process. He promptly read the entire manuscript and let me know where my statements contradicted his research. I appreciate the feedback from my beta readers, interviewees, and members of the Nonfiction Authors Association that helped me finalize the title, subtitle, and cover design.

Thanks to the professionals whose expertise made this book look good: Alan Barnett for cover design and typesetting and Janine Milstrey for creating the interior illustrations based on my charts and diagrams.

Although I'm a professional editor, I knew that I needed to hire a copy editor for this book, and Ariel Hansen came through with edits that went beyond ensuring consistent use of capitalization and fixing typos. Her comments and questions pointed out better ways to communicate my ideas. Elaine Duncan caught more errors with her thorough proofreading. This book wouldn't have been complete without a comprehensive index, for which I thank Judi Gibbs.

This book contains excerpts from blog posts I published on my website and from an article I wrote for *Screen Printing Magazine* in 2016, "The Migration of Printed Electronics to 3D," which was voted Best in Class in the SGIA/ Academy of Screen and Digital Print Technologies 2017 technical writing competition.

FOR FURTHER READING

This section includes works mentioned in the manuscript plus a few additional suggestions.

Books

Biello, David. *The Unnatural World: The Race to Remake Civilization in Earth's Newest Age*. New York: Scribner, 2016.

Cohen, Ben and Jerry Greenfield. *Ben & Jerry's Double-Dip: How to Run a Values-Led Business and Make Money, Too*. New York: Simon & Schuster, 1997.

Edmondson, Brad. *Ice Cream Social: The Struggle for the Soul of Ben and Jerry's*. San Francisco: Berrett-Koehler Publishers, 2014.

Esty, Daniel and Andrew Winston. *Green to Gold: How Smart Companies Use Environmental Strategy to Innovate, Create Value, and Build Competitive Advantage*. New Haven, CT: Yale University Press, 2006.

Freinkel, Susan. *Plastic: A Toxic Love Story*. New York: Houghton Mifflin Harcourt, 2011.

Geiser, Ken. *Materials Matter: Toward a Sustainable Materials Policy*. Cambridge, MA: The MIT Press, 2001.

Hawken, Paul. *The Ecology of Commerce (Revised Edition)*. New York: HarperCollins, 2010.

Highsmith, Andrew. *Demolition Means Progress: Flint, Michigan, and the Fate of the American Metropolis*. Chicago: University of Chicago Press, 2015.

Howard, Steven. *Leadership Lessons from the Volkswagen Saga*. Palm Springs, CA: Caliente Press, 2017.

London, Bernard. *Ending the Depression Through Planned Obsolescence.* New York: printed by the author, 1932. https://babel.hathitrust.org/cgi/pt?id=wu .89097035273;view=1up;seq=10. Also bound as a book in the University of Wisconsin-Madison Memorial Library.

McDonough, William and Michael Braungart. *Cradle to Cradle: Remaking the Way We Make Things.* New York: North Point Press, 2002.

McDonough, William and Michael Braungart. *The Upcycle: Beyond Sustainability—Designing for Abundance.* New York: North Point Press, 2013.

Menzel, Peter and Charles Mann. *Material World: A Global Family Portrait.* San Francisco: Sierra Club Books, 1994.

Miodownik, Mark. *Stuff Matters: Exploring the Marvelous Materials That Shape Our Man-Made World.* Boston: Houghton Mifflin Harcourt, 2014.

Moore, Kate. *The Radium Girls: The Dark Story of America's Shining Women.* Naperville, IL: Sourcebooks, Inc., 2017.

Patnaik, Dev. *Wired to Care: How Companies Prosper When They Create Widespread Empathy.* Upper Saddle River, New Jersey: FT Press, 2009.

SanClements, Michael. *Plastic Purge: How to Use Less Plastic, Eat Better, Keep Toxins Out of Your Body, and Help Save the Sea Turtles!* New York: St. Martin's Griffin, 2014.

Smil, Vaclav. *Making the Modern World: Materials and Dematerialization.* West Sussex, UK: John Wiley & Sons, 2014.

Winkless, Laurie. *Science and the City: The Mechanics Behind the Metropolis.* London: Bloomsbury Sigma, 2016.

Articles

Ali, Saleem, et al. "Mineral Supply for Sustainable Development Requires Resource Governance." *Nature* 543 (2017): 367.

Andrady, Anthony L. "Microplastics in the marine environment." *Marine Pollution Bulletin* 62 (2011): 1596.

Billrey, Jenna. "BPA-Free Plastic Containers May Be Just as Hazardous." *Scientific American*, August 11, 2014.

Bombelli, Paolo, Christopher J. Howe, and Federica Bertocchini. "Polyethylene bio-degradation by caterpillars of the wax moth Galleria mellonella." *Current Biology* 27 (2017): PR292-93. https://doi.org/10.1016/j.cub.2017.02.060.

Cole, Matthew, Pennie Lindeque, Claudia Halsband, and Tamara S. Galloway. "Microplastics as contaminants in the marine environment: A review." *Marine Pollution Bulletin* 62 (2011): 2588.

Geyer, Roland, Jenna R. Jambeck, and Kara Lavender Law. "Production, Use, and Fate of All Plastics Ever Made." *Science Advances* 3, no. 7 (2017). https://doi.org/10.1126/sciadv.1700782.

National Geographic Society, s.v. "Great Pacific Garbage Patch," ed. Jeannie Evers, accessed January 7, 2019. https://www.nationalgeographic.org/encyclopedia/great-pacific-garbage-patch/

Rich, Nathaniel. "The Lawyer Who Became DuPont's Worst Nightmare." *New York Times*, January 6, 2016. https://www.nytimes.com/2016/01/10/magazine/the-lawyer-who-became-duponts-worst-nightmare.html.

INDEX

Page numbers with an *f* refer to a figure.

Author photograph © Dan Devries

ABOUT THE AUTHOR

Julia L F Goldstein holds a PhD in materials science and started her career as an engineer before migrating to journalism in 2001. She now writes white papers and other technical marketing content for companies manufacturing a wide variety of products. Julia is active in her local writing community and leads the Seattle chapter of the Nonfiction Authors Association. When she's not writing, she enjoys playing flute and piccolo and participating in triathlons.

Connect with the author: juliagoldsteinauthor.com
Follow her on Twitter: @jlfgoldstein

Did you enjoy this book? Post a review on Amazon and Goodreads.

CPSIA information can be obtained
at www.ICGtesting.com
Printed in the USA
FFHW012036030419
51444098-56887FF